GREAT EXPECTATIONS
EIGHT SHORT PLAYS
ABOUT TEENS UNDER PRESSURE

by Nicole B. Adkins, Will Coleman, Anne
G'Fellers-Mason, Laura King, Wendy-Marie Martin,
Marshall N. Opie, Jeri Weiss and Ricky Young-Howze

www.youthplays.com
info@youthplays.com
424-703-5315

LIST OF PLAYS

I'm Totally Getting Sent to Bible Camp This Summer by Ricky Young-Howze

Room for Two by Jeri Weiss

Holding by Nicole B. Adkins

The Morgan Show by Laura King

Speech & Debate by Will Coleman

Sweet Dreams by Wendy-Marie Martin

The Summoning Sky by Marshall N. Opie

The Dance We Do by Anne G'Fellers-Mason

PRODUCTION NOTES

Great Expectations is a collection of short plays exploring the pressures teen face from parents and guardians, and sometimes even from themselves. The plays can be performed as individual pieces or grouped together in any combination to create a show of the desired length and performed under the title *Great Expectations*.

PRODUCTION HISTORY

Great Expectations was conceived and developed at Hollins University in the Playwriting graduate program by the 2014 Writing for Young Audiences class, taught by Nicole B. Adkins.

The class self-produced the first staged reading and workshop on July 28, 2014 at Mill Mountain Theatre, in collaboration with Hollins University and Roanoke Children's Theatre. Special thanks to RCT Education Director Meghan Griffith for

organizing the wonderful team of young actors/responders.
The reading was directed by Wendy-Marie Martin with the following cast:

Savannah Amos, Brynn Chavira, Julian Davis, Elise Guilfoyle, Taylor Herndon, Julia Holland, Sarah Mead, DeShawn Riley, Emma Sala, Nathan Smith, Sophie Sons, Gwyneth Strope, Camryn Sullivan, Kalley Sullivan, and Mayme Todd.

Great Expectations premiered at Overland High School (Aurora, CO) on February 12, 2015. It was directed by Eric E. Eidson and stage managed by Rinesty Rusli, with the following cast:

Mohammed Ahmad, Alissa Austin, Anna Austin, Megan Faktorovich, Noah Johnston, Rebecca Martin, Jasmine Middleton, Samuel Pierce III, D'Angelo Rivas, Rinesty Rusli, Taylor Vaughn, and Katherine Young.

I'M TOTALLY GETTING SENT TO BIBLE CAMP THIS SUMMER

A short dramedy by
Ricky Young-Howze

CAST OF CHARACTERS

PETER, 17. Boy. Looks like he stepped out of a Norman Rockwell painting.

NATALIE, 17 and a half. Girl. Punk-Rocker.

SETTING

Peter's backyard.

(Natalie and Peter sneak onstage. They are wearing Prom Formal. Peter is holding a large laundry bag.)

PETER: Are we alone?

NATALIE: We're not getting away with this yet. Let's move quick.

(Natalie quickly removes Peter's tie and suit jacket. She kisses him.)

PETER: I'm totally getting sent to Bible Camp this summer. My mom is going to kill me.

NATALIE: I still can't believe you snuck out. Maybe I'm dating a bad boy after all.

PETER: I'm bad to the bone, baby. I snuck out. Stayed out until one in the morning. And do you know what I'm going to do next?

NATALIE: What?

(Peter kisses her again. He picks up the bag and starts to go through it.)

PETER: That. Man this feels so good. Did you notice that even when we sat down to eat our burgers I didn't even say the grace?

NATALIE: You're just a rebel.

(Peter starts to unbutton his shirt. We find that he is wearing a pair of footie pajamas underneath.)

You should get in quick. Your mom is going to kill you if she wakes up and doesn't see you in bed.

PETER: Well she should have let me go to Prom in the first place. But if I'm fast maybe I've got a shot to pull this off.

NATALIE: You said she called me a heathen? She doesn't even know me.

(Peter starts to take off his suit pants but his shoes get in the way. His legs get tangled and he topples over.)

PETER: All she needs to know is that she doesn't see you in a pew every Sunday morning. She's always seen me marrying a good Christian girl and going to medical school.

(Natalie grabs his shoes and starts pulling them off.)

NATALIE: And what did you see?

PETER: I see that blood creeps me out. And people like my mom are just...high.

NATALIE: What do you mean by that?

(Peter is now wearing a full pair of childish pajamas. He stands up to adjust himself.)

PETER: If you have your head so high up in heaven everyone else just looks like ants and you forget that they're people too. Me? I personally always liked being one of the ants.

NATALIE: I don't know whether to be flattered or insulted to be called an ant.

PETER: I'd be flattered, I'd be really flattered.

(They kiss again. This one is more serious than the last. Peter steps away. Natalie drapes his tie around her neck.)

NATALIE: Is this your first time?

(Peter looks at her weirdly.)

To kiss someone I mean.

PETER: No not really...I kissed a girl once...on the cheek.

(Natalie tries his suit coat on for size.)

NATALIE: Oh...I kinda wanted to be your first.

PETER: Am I your first?

NATALIE: No, but I like it. How do I look?

PETER: Silly. I'm glad. Glad you like it I mean.

NATALIE: *(Spinning on her heel:)* Well am I worth all of this? Getting into all of this trouble with your mom?

PETER: Worth every bit.

(Natalie sits down in the grass.)

NATALIE: You're such a sweetheart.

PETER: Why?

NATALIE: You promposed with a single rose with a note. Seriously "check yes or no"? People still do that? Your hand stayed on mine the entire time. And then we danced that box step with enough room to breathe between us.

(Peter sits beside her.)

PETER: It's the only dance I know. I didn't think you would like that bumping and...grinding.

NATALIE: A lot of boys would be...a lot of boys have.

PETER: Do you know why I loved being with you?

(Natalie puts her head on his shoulder.)

NATALIE: Why?

PETER: You don't look behind you—like you're not worried about listening. My mom can hear foul language from a mile away. You never know when a church member is in the booth behind you, waiting to tell on you.

NATALIE: If you spend your life always watching what you're doing you don't have time to enjoy the view.

PETER: But where is the shame?

NATALIE: Shame of what?

PETER: Exactly...there's shame everywhere. That's all they see.

NATALIE: Am I such a bad person for seeing more?

PETER: Not to me.

(Peter puts all of his clothes in the bag. Natalie proffers the suit jacket. She passes the tie, but he closes her hand around it and pushes her hand away. She smiles.)

NATALIE: It sucks so bad that you're going to be punished for all of this. You didn't even do anything wrong.

PETER: You know that and I know that but...

(He shrugs.)

NATALIE: If I knew that I was going to catch all of this just because I went out with you then I'd be looking to do something to deserve the punishment I was getting.

PETER: I'm getting everything I deserve I assure you.

NATALIE: And then you say sweet things like that.

(Peter pulls a long rope out of the bag.)

PETER: I should really be sneaking in now.

(Natalie lounges back in the grass.)

NATALIE: Or, you know, you could not go in at all.

PETER: What?

NATALIE: You know, find one of the after parties. A place to crash. Together.

PETER: I don't really know...

(They share a look. Peter looks uncertain.)

NATALIE: *(Quietly:)* It doesn't have to be a party. It could just be you and me. You know, crashing.

PETER: Natalie...

(Natalie rises and comes close. She drapes the tie around his neck and pulls him in close. She runs her hand down his back lower and lower until he stops her.)

No. Not like this.

NATALIE: *(With a sly smile:)* It's prom night.

PETER: I want to...I mean look at you!

NATALIE: You can't be serious.

PETER: One day, when we're ready?

(Peter is about to leave but Natalie stops him. She reaches up and roughs up his hair.)

NATALIE: There. A perfect bed head. Your mom is going to kill you but she sure does have a sweet boy.

PETER: I try my best.

NATALIE: If she doesn't deport you to Bible Camp or kill you right away...give me a call.

PETER: Of course. I should go in now.

NATALIE: Yes you should.

(They share one last kiss. They hold hands as long as they can before Peter finally crosses offstage. Natalie drapes the tie around her neck. She starts to walk away.)

Any other guy...

(End of play.)

The Author Speaks

What inspired you to write this play?
When I was a teen I was under a lot of pressure from my conservative Christian family to always be a "good kid." Sometimes I was punished for doing the moral thing just because it wasn't the "right" thing to do. When I worked in a church I saw that happening with a new generation of kids. All these kids had a sense of right and wrong and were all great kids but they were put under a lot of pressure to be perfect and were not given any space to mess up. So I wanted to write a play about the kids I knew and how some respond to this pressure.

Was the structure or other elements of the play influenced by any other work?
One of the first playwrights that I ever read was Neil Simon, so I always take a page from his book when it comes to writing dialogue. Sometimes the most romantic and funny things come from people saying things in their own vocabulary and building off of what the other has to say. Simon created a tapestry of words that always made me jealous. In every piece I try to give every character their own unique way of saying things and let their reactions to what is said make up the core of the story.

Have you dealt with the same theme in other works that you have written?
Since I was born in the Bible Belt, I'm always drawing from my experiences with religion and southern pride in my work. A lot of my plays have to do with people struggling with repression, morality, conservatism, or their identity in a conservative place. Most people get their identities from where they live but I like to highlight in my work the people

who may be disenfranchised in that group but still forced to live there.

What writers have had the most profound effect on your style?
Neil Simon has had the most profound effect on my work as far as how to construct a scene and what makes good dialogue. Cherie Bennett and Jeff Gottesfeld and their plays for teens have always inspired me because they best show how to write plays for teens without making them too superficial or corny. They show that teens can deal with hard issues and make strong characters. Whenever I'm writing a new play, I'm going back to one of these playwrights to see if they did what I'm trying to do only better.

What do you hope to achieve with this work?
I want to show people the kind of pressure that they put kids under these days. This generation of kids is one of the smartest, most responsible, and socially aware that we've ever seen and we never like to put a lot of faith in them. I want adults who see this play to know that teens are capable of making moral decisions. I want teens watching and performing this play to know that they're not alone when they think they're feeling the pressure.

What were the biggest challenges involved in the writing of this play?
The biggest challenge was remembering that I'm not a kid anymore and that what I remember from my teen years is not so hip anymore. I had to really talk to the teens I know and ask them what romance means to them in their world and if prom has the same pressures and problems for them that it had for me back in the day. The idea of promposing was foreign to me until a couple of kids in a reading asked me how Peter asked

Natalie to the prom. So my biggest problem in revision was finding a common ground in my teen years and what kids are experiencing today.

What are the most common mistakes that occur in productions of your work?
I would say tone. My work tends to be straightforward and sometimes jokes and humor are lost among the performers until they read it a third time. In the past, pacing was a problem. I like to use a lot of stage directions in my play and sometimes actors like to rush through them without being in the moment. It's usually fixed by just taking your time.

What inspired you to become a playwright?
I was inspired to become a playwright in high school. Our theatre teacher's husband would write the best plays for us to perform that would never see printing or the kind of audiences he deserved. We were also in the first high school production of *A Heart Divided* by Cherie Bennett and Jeff Gottesfeld and I got to meet Jeff and hear him talk about the play. My junior year I wrote my first play and had it performed and from then on I was hooked. Years later I'm still finding the same amount of joy writing that I did back then.

How did you research the subject?
The subject required little research. It's based upon my own experiences as a teen. I grew up in a conservative household, so I know what it's like to have friends that don't fit with your parents' ideals. I did pick the brain of several teens to make sure that I wasn't dating myself with my language.

Are any characters modeled after real life or historical figures?
These characters were inspired by many of the teens that I encountered by working in churches and group homes. No one kid is all good or all bad. So when I came up with an idea for Peter, I wanted to show an everyday kid who is not just a bundle of hormones but a kid with the beginnings of his own moral compass and a bearing he wants to go on. The same goes for Natalie. All I wanted to show is someone who is not all bad but with a moral compass that just doesn't point to the "true north" Peter's mom might like it to.

Do any films/videos exist of prior productions of this play?
Sadly no. I was informed that the production at Overland High School went over great. The director told me that several of the girls awwed at Peter's lines. Surprisingly, the director told me that the boys in the audience identified with Peter. They liked that Peter was proof that boys didn't just want "one thing."

Shakespeare gave advice to the players in *Hamlet*; if you could give advice to your cast what would it be?
Take your time and have fun with it. You don't have to rush through stage directions and you don't have to say lines too slowly. These characters are speaking from the heart even if they don't know the right words to express themselves. And find the funny, awkward, and dorkily romantic moments. Embrace them and own them!

How was the first production different from the vision that you created in your mind?
I sadly didn't get to see it but I hear that it was done wonderfully. It was done as an assembly show with other 10-minute plays in front of 500 students in their high school. That

was actually better than any first production that I could have thought of. Winning over ticket-paying audiences and critics is one thing but winning over 500 rowdy school kids is really a testament to your work. And it meant it was in front of the very kids that I wanted to reach.

Why do you always write romance?
The true answer is that I never start a play thinking that a romance is going to be at the center of it. I just love finding characters that are passionate and find that same passion mirrored in someone else. I also feel that most of the romances that you see in mainstream media today aren't very good. That means every romance that I do write means that I'm adding a good tearjerker into the mix.

About the Author

Ricky Young-Howse is a playwright, director, and blogger from New Jersey. He is a transplant from Tennessee where he attended Austin Peay State University where he earned a B.S. in Theatre Performance with a minor in Design. There he was awarded the honor of "Most Outstanding Exiting Senior of Theatre and Dance." He is an MFA Playwright from Hollins University.

ROOM FOR TWO

A short drama by
Jeri Weiss

CAST OF CHARACTERS

JEN, female, 15. Her mother has recently remarried after a nasty divorce, and she expects her daughter to be friends with her sullen stepsister.

LISSA, female, 15. Her mother passed away several years ago, and she is having difficulty adjusting to her father's remarriage.

SETTING

A bedroom, with two distinct sides.

(A bedroom shared by two teenage girls. JEN is on her side of the room, arguing with her mother on her cell phone.)

JEN: *(On cell phone:)* I *have* been trying. *(Beat.)* Yes, I have! Just because you married her dad doesn't mean— *(Beat.)* Well, I don't know what else you expect me to do. I gave up half my room. I tried introducing her to my friends, and she just sits there and never says anything. She's the one who isn't trying. *(Beat.)* How much more time? She's been here three weeks already and— *(Beat.)* Well, it's not my fault her mom is—

(LISSA enters, sullenly. Did she hear what Jen just said? Jen's not sure. She tries to compensate by greeting Lissa warmly.)

Hi, Lissa!

LISSA: *(Barely acknowledging Jen:)* Hi.

(Lissa lies on her bed.)

JEN: *(On phone, quietly:)* Yes, she just walked in. *(Beat.)* Fine. I'll try harder.

(Jen tries to engage Lissa by rolling her eyes at her mom's lecture.)

(On cell phone:) Yes. Okay. I will. I will. I will...

(Lissa ignores the conversation and rolls over so her back is to Jen.)

(On cell phone:) Okay, bye.

(Jen tosses her cell phone on her bed. She makes another attempt to bond with her stepsister.)

(To Lissa:) Mothers! Right?

(Lissa rolls over and stares incredulously at Jen.)

(Wishing she could take it back:) Oh uh...sorry. I didn't mean to...

(Lissa rolls back over toward the wall. Jen tries again.)

How was your day?

LISSA: What?

JEN: Did you have a good day?

LISSA: *(With no emotion:)* Yeah. It was a great day.

JEN: Great? — That's much better than good. *(Goofy:)* Progress — yay!

(Lissa does not crack a smile. Jen, fighting frustration, stops her attempt at conversation.)

(She begins putting things away while quietly singing a hymn. [Note: any hymn may be substituted.])

(Singing:) AVE MARIA...

(Lissa, recognizing the song, rises in bed. Clearly, it affects her.)

(Singing:) GRATIA PLENA —

LISSA: *(Cutting her off:)* Do you think you could keep it down a little?

JEN: What? I was barely making a sound.

LISSA: I can't concentrate with you —

JEN: Concentrate on what?

LISSA: I'm trying to...

(Lissa looks around, sees a book, and picks it up.)

I'm trying to read.

JEN: *(Not buying it:)* You're trying to read.

LISSA: That's right.

JEN: We'll I'm trying to practice my solo for church this Sunday.

LISSA: I hate that song.

JEN: Well, I happen to like it.

(Jen goes back to what she was doing, quietly singing the hymn.)

AVE MARIA...

(Lissa tries to find her headphones. She digs through her things, loudly opening and closing drawers, unzipping bags, etc.)

(Jen, thinking Lissa is doing this on purpose, sings louder. The more Jen's volume increases, the more agitated Lissa gets.)

GRATIA PLENA...

(Lissa frantically looks for something, anything, with which to lash out against Jen.)

(She picks up her water bottle [or other item] and throws it at Jen, narrowly missing her.)

What the— What is wrong with you?

LISSA: I asked you nicely—

JEN: Nicely? You haven't done or said one nice thing since you moved in here. What is your problem?

LISSA: I don't have a problem. I'm sitting here quietly and you're being rude.

JEN: Rude? Seriously? I've gone out of my way to try to make you feel welcome. I've introduced you to all my friends—

LISSA: Your friends are freaks—

JEN: You're the freak; not them. All you do is lie around all day, moping. I invited you to go with us to the mall, to the movies, to every flipping party. You don't want to do anything. *(Sarcastically:)* And when you do grace us with your presence, you sit around with this snarly look on your face all the time.

(Lissa snarls.)

See? See? There it is.

(Lissa buries her ears in her pillows, trying to drown out Jen.)

Don't ignore me. You're going to listen to this.

(Jen pulls at Lissa's pillows. Lissa struggles to keep them on her ears.)

LISSA: Get away from me!

(Their fight gets more physical, with pushing and shoving, until Jen falls on the floor.)

(The girls stare at each other with hatred in their eyes. Jen is seething now. She resumes her singing to spite Lissa.)

JEN: *(Singing, loudly:)* DOMINUS TECUM...

LISSA: *(Completely losing it:)* Stop it! Stop it; stop it; stop it!

(Jen stops, confused by Lissa's explosive reaction.)

JEN: What is it, you psycho?!

(Lissa's outburst seems to have released something bottled up inside her for a long time, maybe years. She becomes inconsolable.)

(Jen doesn't know what to do.)

Should I... Do you want me to call your dad?

(Lissa, crying, shakes her head. Jen watches her helplessly.)

(Lissa takes some deep breaths, trying to compose herself. Jen hands her a box of tissues.)

LISSA: Thank you. *(Embarrassed:)* That song... It was my mom's favorite...

JEN: *(Realizing the significance:)* Oh... I didn't—

LISSA: They sang it at... When she...

JEN: I'm really sorry... *(Pointing to the door:)* Do you want me to leave you—

LISSA: No. I'm okay.

JEN: You don't exactly seem okay.

LISSA: I don't think I've heard it since... I'd forgotten all about it.

JEN: Maybe... Maybe I could ask Pastor Ruth for a different solo.

LISSA: It's okay. You don't have to...

JEN: There's plenty of other hymns—

LISSA: It's a good song. You should sing it.

JEN: Not if—

LISSA: It's good to remember. *(Beat.)* Sometimes I'm afraid I'll forget her completely.

(There is an awkward silence. Jen sits next to Lissa.)

JEN: I should have been more...understanding.

(Lissa shakes it off.)

LISSA: I'm sure divorce isn't easy either.

JEN: It isn't. I hardly ever see my dad anymore.

LISSA: Yeah, I was wondering...

JEN: New kids.

(Lissa nods.)

But it's not like... I mean, at least he isn't...

LISSA: Yeah.

(More silence. Then:)

Death sucks.

(Jen nods. After a beat:)

JEN: Sometimes life does too.

(Lissa nods. They sit side-by-side, taking it all in. Jen takes Lissa's hand.)

(Lights fade. End of play.)

The Author Speaks

What inspired you to write this play?
I was given a prompt to write a play about the effect parental expectations have on teenagers. I thought the story of two girls who are forced to share a room would make a compelling story—it just screams conflict. I was inspired to set the play in a stepfamily situation because, as a stepparent myself, I knew there would be a wealth of complex emotions to explore. I know first-hand how difficult it is for families to blend, especially for the children, who have no control of the situation.

What do you hope to achieve with this work?
At the beginning of the play, Jen and Lissa think they have nothing in common. Jen is outgoing and Lissa keeps to herself. Throughout the course of the play, they realize that even though their losses are different, the pain they feel is similar. My hope is that this play will ring true for teens who are dealing with the pain of divorce or death. Even though there is no easy remedy, I hope that it helps teens realize there are others out there going through the same thing. I hope this brings them comfort.

What were the biggest challenges involved in the writing of this play?
Fitting all the material I wanted to cover on this topic within ten minutes was challenging. At first I covered a lot of territory and the resolution felt like it happened too fast, like the solution came too easily. After numerous drafts, I realized that the resolution didn't have to be a major revelation; it could be something smaller and simpler. Jen and Lissa will no doubt have their ups and downs, but the simple act of

compassion shown with the clasping of hands at the end was a much better choice.

How did you research the subject?

Having been a teenage girl myself, and having survived the teen years of my daughter and stepdaughter, I had many real-life experiences to draw from. I'm an introvert and I value my privacy, so the thought of having to share my room with someone I barely knew was horrifying. I thought about how I would respond if I were put into their situation. I also thought about some of the difficulties my stepdaughter had adjusting to the divorce and remarriage of her parents. I pulled from the emotions we all experienced when she came to live with us.

Shakespeare gave advice to the players in *Hamlet*; if you could give advice to your cast what would it be?

After directing a few of my own plays, I have come to value the input from my actors and have sometimes found them to have a better understanding of their characters than I do! While the dialogue should not be changed without the playwright's permission, I think there is more flexibility with the stage directions. I would suggest to my cast that they experiment with the way the two characters physically interact with each other. The fight can be choreographed in a way that works best for the actors within the boundaries of the set.

About the Author

Jeri Weiss is a Northern California playwright whose work has been published and produced throughout the United States and Canada. She received an Ivey Award following the Minneapolis premiere of **Before You Speak**, which explores bullying and school violence. Her controversial gun play, **Run Jane Run**, was a regional finalist in the Kennedy Center

America College Theatre Festival, and her dark satire *The Procedure*, set in a misogynistic society, was selected by the Stella Adler Studio of Acting in its search for plays with social impact. Jeri's work has been published by YouthPLAYS, Freshwater Press, and Applause Theatre & Cinema Books. She is an MFA candidate in the Playwright's Lab at Hollins University and a member of the Dramatists Guild.

HOLDING

A short dramedy by
Nicole B. Adkins

CAST OF CHARACTERS

ALISON, female, a junior in high school, feels pressure to be perfect.

CATE, female, a junior in high school, struggling with a life-changing secret.

TERRANCE, male, a junior in high school, Cate's boyfriend.

PETE, male, a junior in high school, Alison's love-interest, lives with his aunt.

ALISON'S MOM, female, expects Alison to make good decisions and wants the best for her.

CATE'S BIG BROTHER, male, hopes Cate will break out of the family pattern.

TERRANCE'S DAD, male, doesn't really mind Terrance getting into minimal trouble as long as he doesn't get caught or upset his mom.

PETE'S AUNT, female, Pete's guardian and aunt, also has three small children.

PRODUCTION NOTES

This play is designed to be performed by young adults. The four actors playing older characters should wear half masks to portray the adult/older characters. These masks should be very simple, in no way silly or gaudy. The adult roles should be performed honestly and directly, with no attempt to seem older or play a "character."

(Lights up on ALISON, PETE, CATE, and TERRANCE, four high school juniors, two couples. CATE'S BIG BROTHER, TERRANCE'S DAD, ALISON'S MOM and PETE'S AUNT are present in the background, wearing masks. They are meant to be played by actors the same age as the other characters. Each "parent" figure is only in the mind of their child/charge. They are never acknowledged in the scene. As the play progresses, they should move closer and closer to the four teens.)

ALISON: We are criminals. We are criminals!

PETE: It's OK, it's OK.

ALISON: Says Pete.

CATE: Are you saying that for her benefit, or yours?

PETE: *(Slight beat.)* Yes. And it's all going to be OK.

ALISON: Says Pete—who climbed a TREE when the cops came! You CLIMBED A TREE! It's fall, you idiot! There aren't even any leaves! What, did you think they were going to mistake you for a squirrel?? Now I know how you react in a crisis.

PETE: I know, I know... I just... I did the first thing that came into my head.

TERRANCE: It's cool, man.

ALISON: Dumb!

PETE'S AUNT: I can't leave the house in the middle of the night, Pete! Wake up three small children? For this? When I took you in I thought you were a good, smart boy! Was I wrong about you?

ALISON: Anyway here we are. Awaiting our fates.

CATE: They put us in their break room, Alison. I'm pretty sure that door doesn't even have a lock. But they've gotta have donuts stashed away someplace... Ugh, so hungry.

(She stands and starts to look around the room.)

TERRANCE: Cate —

ALISON: Are you crazy! They told us to stay put! Don't you move. Get back in your seat!

CATE: As if they are taking us seriously when there are actual criminals out there in the world. We're just a handful of dumb kids caught out past curfew. What are they going to do, lock me up for stretching my legs?

ALISON: What if they press charges?! What if this goes on some kind of permanent record?! We were caught out past curfew drinking! We are juniors, you guys, this year is crucial!

CATE: Wine coolers. We were drinking WINE COOLERS in a PARK! We'll probably just get a warning. Trust me, my brother's gotten like three of them. There are much bigger things to worry about in life.

ALISON: This seems pretty big to me!

ALISON'S MOM: Yes, Alison. You can spend the night at Cate's. But I expect you to make smart decisions. Meaning: none of the decisions you've been making lately whenever Cate is involved. This is your last chance. Understand? And don't stay up too late. You have that soccer tournament tomorrow. If you play things right this year you might just have a chance at a scholarship. We need that. This is your future at stake.

CATE'S BIG BROTHER: You're talented, you know that sis? You could get out of here. Seriously, get out of here. Don't get sucked down into the mud. I'll probably never leave this town.

But you could. You should. If you don't I'll kick your scrawny little butt.

CATE: Seriously people, if we were going to get busted it should have been for something more worthwhile than strawberry pee-water.

TERRANCE: Hey, I only had 10 dollars. I told the lady to buy the cheapest stuff she could get. You know. So we could have more.

PETE: I got you, man.

CATE: Dumb. And no donuts. How could they be out of donuts? What kind of third-rate police station is this anyway!

ALISON: They called my mom... They called my MOM! Oh my god. I wonder when she'll get here. I wonder how much time I have left on this earth. She is going to disown me.

CATE: She'll get over it. She always does.

ALISON: Not this time.

PETE'S AUNT: This is the last straw, Pete.

PETE: I hope I don't get kicked out.

TERRANCE: I'm probably going to be grounded until I die. Honestly I bet my dad wouldn't have cared if we hadn't gotten caught.

TERRANCE'S DAD: Yeah sure, you can spend the night at Pete's. Here's 10 bucks, son. Stay outta trouble.

TERRANCE: It's my mom I worry about. She's going to give me that "who are you, what did you do with my son" look. I'd rather hear Dad yelling any day.

TERRANCE'S DAD: Damnit, Terrance, keep it together, will you? Just keep it together, and don't upset your mom. She thinks you hung the moon.

CATE: My Mom'll just ignore it like she does everything else that happens to me.

ALISON: *(Beat.)* This didn't exactly happen to you, Cate. The whole thing was sort of your idea.

CATE: Nobody dragged you along, Miss Perfect. Besides, you drank more than anybody.

ALISON: Did not! I came for moral support.

CATE: Some of that would be great right about now!

ALISON: And I wanted to see Pete. *(To Pete, who looks grateful:)* Which doesn't mean I'm over being mad at you.

TERRANCE: *(To Cate:)* What does she mean, moral support?

ALISON: You need to tell him. Before our parents get here and you miss your chance.

PETE: Tell him what?   **TERRANCE:** Tell me what?

CATE: That *Alison* is a lightweight who needs to mind her own business. *(To Pete, changing subject:)* What are you going to do? I hope they don't make you spend the night.

TERRANCE: Maybe they'll let you come with me and my dad.

PETE: I don't think it works that way. Besides, your dad is terrifying. That might be worse than the rest of the night here.

TERRANCE'S DAD: I thought you were smarter than this!

CATE'S BIG BROTHER: You're supposed to be smarter than this, Cate.

ALISON'S MOM: I can't even look at you, Alison.

PETE'S AUNT: ...

ALL FOUR "PARENT" FIGURES: What were you thinking??

(Terrance brings his chair and puts it beside Cate's. Terrance tries to take Cate's hand. She pulls away.)

PETE: *(To Alison:)* I'm really sorry about the tree. I panicked. It was dumb. It'll never happen again.

ALISON: Yeah. Mostly because us getting to see each other will never happen again as long as we live. Which may be only the next 15 minutes.

PETE: *(Beat.)* Well...if the world's about to end I'd better get something off my chest...

ALISON: OK...?

PETE: I just—I...tonight was really great. Before the whole...arrest thing I mean. I really like you.

ALISON: *(Beat.)* I like you too. Even if you are kind of an idiot.

PETE: *(Smiling, goofy:)* She likes me! And hey, we can see each other at school.

ALISON: Yeah. If we don't all get sent to juvie!

CATE: Seriously, what world do you live in?

ALISON: Just because you're used to getting in trouble doesn't mean I am!

CATE: Oh, piss off! [Oh, get lost!]

ALISON : I guess my mom was right about you.

CATE: Wow. Keep me away from her. I don't wanna get put away for murder!

TERRANCE: Forget about her. Talk to me.

(Cate finds plastic-packaged salad crackers.)

CATE: Oh thank god. Crackers.

(She opens and eats them.)

ALISON: OMG. Now you are stealing from a police station.

CATE: Stealing?? Really? They give these out free at restaurants!

ALISON: Does this look like a restaurant??

(Cate moves away from Alison, eating her crackers. Terrance follows her.)

TERRANCE: Seriously, c'mon. What's up? What did you need to tell me? Are you mad about the wine coolers or something? You've hardly said three words to me all night. Even before...all this.

CATE: No I'm not mad about the stupid wine coolers.

TERRANCE: What then?

CATE: *(Beat.)* I had this plan for tonight. You were going to have a few drinks...and then I was going to tell you something. But I'm not sure I'm ready to talk about it now.

TERRANCE: *(Beat.)* Are you breaking up with me or something?

CATE: No, you idiot.

TERRANCE: I love you, you know. Whatever it is, I'm here.

CATE: *(Beat.)* Do you know my mom had my brother when she was 16 years old? She didn't even have her driver's license yet, but she had a kid. She was 19 when she had me.

TERRANCE: I didn't know she was that young.

CATE: Yeah.

TERRANCE: What does this have to do with...?

(Cate puts Terrance's hand on her stomach.)

Oh...god...you can't mean...

CATE: Why do you think I didn't drink any of those stupid wine coolers?

CATE'S BIG BROTHER: Don't get stuck here, kid.

TERRANCE'S DAD: Keep your head on your shoulders. Make your mom proud.

PETE'S AUNT: Don't you want your parents to look down and be proud of you?

ALISON'S MOM: You have to want to make something of yourself. Know where you're going. You can do it honey, I know you can. You just have to work at it.

ALL FOUR "PARENT" FIGURES: Think about your future.

(Alison leans on Pete. Terrance holds Cate.)

ALISON: What's the point of being perfect all the time? I want to live my life! Not just be constantly working and waiting for my future, but actually enjoy myself sometimes.

PETE: I just want to get out on my own. I'm saving for that. Then I feel like my life will really start.

ALISON: I don't want to be at home...but I don't want to leave either. I don't know what I want.

PETE: You'll figure it out Alison. You're smart. First thing I noticed about you. Well...mostly the first thing, haha.

ALISON: *(Smiling:)* You'll be fine, Pete. You're a survivor. One of the first things I noticed about you.

CATE: I swore I wasn't going to be like my mom.

TERRANCE: You're not. You're like you.

CATE: What are we going to do?

TERRANCE: I don't know. I'm really scared. But I'm here OK?

(Puts his arms around her.)

I promise not to run away and climb a tree.

(She laughs a little despite herself.)

CATE: *(Beat.)* Sometimes I feel like you're the only solid thing in the world.

PETE: *(Referring to Terrance and Cate:)* What's wrong with them?

ALISON: Not my place.

PETE: *(Calling over to Pete:)* Hey, you OK man? What's wrong?

TERRANCE: Nothin' man. It's all going to be OK. *(To Cate:)* It's all going to be OK.

(The masked figures move close to the teens.)

ALISON: Hear that? Somebody is coming. The door is opening. *(To Pete:)* Oh god... Hold my hand. On second thought, you'd better not.

(They all stand. The lights dim. End of play.)

The Author Speaks

What inspired you to write this play?
When I was a teenager I had an experience that was somewhat similar to the experience of these characters—being out past curfew and caught with alcoholic beverages. Our situation was especially silly because we chose the most highly patrolled neighborhood in the city for our antics. This play is a highly fictionalized account which bears no resemblance to the actual people involved in my incident, but we were all similarly chastened and terrified both by the idea of how our parents would respond and also by how it might affect our futures. (Luckily for us, the effects were only eye-opening and not serious in a long-term way). OK, and one of the guys in our group did indeed try to hide from the police by climbing a tree…but that was too good to leave out.

Was the structure or other elements of the play influenced by any other work?
Masks fascinate me, and I liked the idea of this piece having characters that resembled a Greek chorus in some ways. Though the masked characters in my play are comprised of individual voices rather than speaking as one (as in a traditional Greek chorus), I wanted these characters to have a kind of elemental, universal feel, and to be a group of characters that represented the same basic idea for each of the unmasked characters.

Have you dealt with the same theme in other works that you have written?
I often write about characters who are deciding who they are and who they want to become.

What writers have had the most profound effect on your style?
I have always been a voracious reader. As a kid I spent years reading all the myths, legends, and original fairy tales I could find. I moved from there to authors who explore the mythic and fantastical in their writing (often fantasy or sci-fi), such as George MacDonald, Hans Christian Andersen, Ursula K. Le Guin, Madeleine L'Engle, C.S. Lewis, Lois Lowry, and Ray Bradbury. I also loved authors of classic books with strong female characters, such as Jane Austen and L.M. Montgomery. I was also very strongly affected by my years working as an actor in theatre for young audiences and was amazed to discover the work of playwrights like Suzan Zeder and José Cruz González and to get to perform in scripts like *The Yellow Boat* by David Saar.

What do you hope to achieve with this work?
Each of the teen characters in this play is facing the oncoming future, and struggling with the expectations of others and with how to proceed with life on his/her own terms. This can be a scary process. I love the William Nicholson quote: "We read to know we're not alone," and I think sometimes that same idea can also be applied to theatre. In the case of this play, if one person acting in the play or seeing it from the audience finds some solace in knowing that they aren't the only ones to feel a certain way, then my goal has been achieved.

What were the biggest challenges involved in the writing of this play?
Originally the same characters playing the teens also played each other's adult, masked counterpoints. I liked the way this read, and how it connected these internal voices more fully to the teen characters (as though they were really in their heads), but from a literary standpoint it just didn't quite connect.

Logistically each actor had to play a certain adult (in order for the dialogue & gender pairing to work), but there was no real significance to which teen played which adult. Ultimately I decided to separate those roles, and then realized that the Greek Chorus connection felt a little more effective this way, so it worked out.

What are the most common mistakes that occur in productions of your work?
I try to explore the use of subtext. Because subtext is not always obvious, sometimes ideas and feelings get missed in performance. This can be as much my fault as that of the actors or director – it is always a learning process for me how much I should say and how much I should simply let actors and directors discover on their own. I would encourage actors in any play (not just mine) to really delve into every character's goals and motivations, try to find what makes them say and do the things they do. This said, sometimes reinterpretations work in my favor, as an actor or director may discover an idea or feeling I didn't even know was there, and give the line a much better reading than I had even imagined! Either way, when a producing company and its members do their homework it always shows.

What inspired you to become a playwright?
My father had his undergraduate degree in theatre and owned a video production company through my childhood. My mother was always a poet and a writer, and ran the production company with my dad, writing many of the scripts for commercials, how-to videos and other jobs. Subsequently I spent a lot of time on set, either just hanging around or being thrown into projects as a handy, free actor. I participated in theatre also from a very early age. (My first appearance on stage was as the dove in *Godspell*...if you know the show,

there is no dove. I spent most of the show scratching my tights). Anyway, the theatre bug bit me. I acted, consumed theatre, read every book I could find, and wrote stories and plays from a very early age. Given the combination of my parents' talents, my great respect for both of them, and my love of theatre and literature, being a playwright kind of felt inevitable. Also, though I began as an actor and that influences every play I write, I became far more entranced by creating and peopling entire worlds than actually being onstage myself. I love to try and create worlds and characters that actors, designers, and directors might enjoy bringing to life, and to see what new colors and depth they bring to my initial envisioning.

Are any characters modeled after real life or historical figures?
As I mentioned, the basic premise was inspired by personal experiences, however none of the characters in this piece were based on the actual people involved (though Alison's reactions were probably closest to my own). I did have two friends in high school that got pregnant, and I remember how difficult that was for them. That influenced the play.

Shakespeare gave advice to the players in *Hamlet*; if you could give advice to your cast what would it be?
Figure out what the characters want. Find and explore the different ways they go about getting what they want. Be fearless.

About the Author

Nicole B. Adkins has taught classes and workshops to students of various ages at theatres, K-12 schools, and universities. Her plays have been performed at Hollins

University, Mill Mountain Theatre, Studio Roanoke, Children's Theatre of Charlotte, Creative Drama Children's Theatre in Winston-Salem, NC, SkyPilot Theatre in Los Angeles, the American International School in Guangzhou, China, and other theatres, schools, and museums nationally and abroad. She collaborated with Matt Omasta of Utah State University on a book entitled *Playwriting and Young Audiences: Collected Wisdom and Practical Advice from the Field* (Intellect Press, 2016). Awards include the National Waldo M. and Grace C. Bonderman Award and recognition in the Beverly Hills Theatre Guild Marilyn Hall competition. A Hollins Children's Literature MFA graduate and Playwright's Lab faculty member, Nicole is also a member of Dramatists Guild and TYA/USA. www.nicolebadkins.com

THE MORGAN SHOW

A short dramedy by
Laura King

CAST OF CHARACTERS

MORGAN, male or female, 13-15 years old, lives in his/her own world, which is a much better place to live.

MOTHER, female. Morgan's mother, 30s, frustrated and anxious about Morgan.

FATHER, male. Morgan's father, 30s, fed-up and determined to set Morgan straight.

SETTING

The family dining room.

(Lights up on a dining room table. MOTHER enters. She places three plates in the center of the table.)

MOTHER: Morgan, it's time to set the table.

(Mother exits and reenters with three glasses.)

Morgan, this table isn't going to set itself.

(Mother exits and reenters with silverware, which she drops noisily on the table.)

Morgan!

MORGAN: *(Off:)* Coming, Mother.

(Mother exits. MORGAN enters, crosses to the table, and slowly starts to set the dishes. Gradually, Morgan begins to finesse the job, twirling the plates and flipping the forks.)

Welcome to The Morgan Show. And now here's Morgan the Magnificent. The world champion in table setting. People come from far and wide to see Morgan in action. Did you see that move? I've never seen a plate spin like that. What about the fork flip? No one in the world flips a fork with that kind of finesse. It's a natural talent, ladies and gentlemen. You either got it or you don't. And Morgan's got it.

MOTHER: *(Off:)* Honey, it's time to eat.

FATHER: *(Off:)* Be right there.

MORGAN: What did I tell you? The public is clamoring, clamoring, I say, for a seat at the Morgan table-setting show. It's standing room only.

(Morgan climbs onto a dining room chair. Mother and FATHER enter.)

Come on in, folks. Take a seat. You're in for a treat. Morgan's the best in the biz.

(Mother and Father sit but do not pay attention to Morgan.)

FATHER: Please, pass the salt.

MORGAN: It's going to be something really special.

MOTHER: May I have the pickles?

MORGAN: Morgan's the best.

(Father and Mother continue to prepare their plates. Morgan eyes them curiously.)

Look alive now. You don't want to miss this.

FATHER: Where's Morgan?

MOTHER: I have no idea.

MORGAN: Everyone's here to see Morgan.

FATHER: I don't know what's come over that child.

MOTHER: I know what you mean.

MORGAN: Morgan's astonishing.

FATHER: A C minus in Algebra.

MOTHER: It's inexcusable.

MORGAN: *(More quietly:)* Morgan's amazing.

FATHER: Never takes the trash out without being nagged.

MOTHER: It's exacerbating.

MORGAN: *(Quieter:)* Morgan's astounding.

FATHER: Just texts and watches TV.

MOTHER: It's exhausting.

MORGAN: *(Even more quietly:)* Everyone wants to hear from Morgan.

(During the following, Morgan sinks lower into the chair as the parents search for answers.)

MOTHER: Do you think there's a problem?

FATHER: An issue?

MOTHER: An ailment?

FATHER: A syndrome?

MOTHER: A sickness?

FATHER: A disorder?

MOTHER: A disease?

MORGAN: Everyone wants to know Morgan's secret.

FATHER: I think it's a lack of motivation.

MOTHER: A lack of stick-to-it-ness.

FATHER: A lack of intelligence.

MOTHER: A lack of ability.

(Morgan has continued to sink so that now only Morgan's head is visible above the table.)

MORGAN: *(Whispering:)* The people don't understand how Morgan does it. No one understands.

(Morgan sinks below the table.)

FATHER: I just don't understand that child.

MOTHER: What do you think we should do?

(During the following, Morgan becomes increasingly agitated.)

FATHER: We need to get tough.

MOTHER: Be firm.

FATHER: Stand together.

MOTHER: Accept no excuses.

FATHER: Take the bull by the horns.

MOTHER: Bite the bullet.

FATHER: It's time for us to say...

MOTHER AND FATHER: Morgan, get your act together.

(Morgan throws the table over. Dishes scatter. Mother and Father do not notice.)

MORGAN: No!

FATHER: No.

MOTHER: No?

FATHER: We have to face it.

MOTHER: There's nothing we can do.

FATHER: Just wait it out.

MOTHER: Hope for the best.

FATHER: Keep the faith.

MOTHER: Wait for the curtain to fall.

MORGAN: *(Dejectedly:)* Welcome to The Morgan Show.

FATHER: Do you have the salt?

MOTHER: Do you have the pickles?

FATHER: I'll get the salt.

MOTHER: I'll get the pickles.

(Mother and Father exit. Morgan slowly puts the table upright again.)

MORGAN: And now here's Morgan the...

(Morgan repositions the chairs around the table.)

The world champion in...

(Morgan places the glasses on the table.)

People come from far and wide...

(Morgan sets the dishes with no finesse. Mother enters carrying pickles.)

MOTHER: Morgan, there you are. You're doing a nice job on the table.

(Father enters carrying salt.)

FATHER: Well, look at you. Good to see you doing what you're supposed to.

MOTHER: Come on now. Let's have a nice quiet dinner.

(They all cross to the table and sit.)

FATHER: Now, isn't this just right?

MOTHER: Everything is as it should be.

(Mother and Father begin to eat. Morgan watches them.)

Please, pass the salt.

(Morgan picks up the salt.)

FATHER: May I have the pickles?

(Morgan picks up the pickles. Mother and Father look at Morgan.)

MOTHER AND FATHER: Morgan?

(Morgan slowly grins, jumps up on the chair, and begins juggling, twirling, or otherwise finessing the pickles and salt.)

MORGAN: Welcome to The Morgan Show. Where nothing is as it should be but everything is just right.

(Blackout. End of play.)

The Author Speaks

What inspired you to write this play?
I wrote *The Morgan Show* for my daughter. I was aware how sometimes what makes her special was being overlooked because of the pressures of school and home. I thought this was probably true for most teenagers. As grown-ups, we tend to focus on what we think our children need to do instead of the wonderful things they already do.

Have you dealt with the same theme in other works that you have written?
I often write about the secret lives of people and how those secrets make them special. I wrote another 10-minute play for young actors called *The Disappointments,* which deals with a brother and sister trying to find their own talents. Just as Morgan from *The Morgan Show* finds solace in the table-setting act, Eli and Amy from *The Disappointments* find solace in their not-too-perfect song-and-dance act.

What do you hope to achieve with this work?
In a small way, I want to give a voice to those teenagers who feel overlooked or criticized by their parents. Morgan is a way for me to show that everyone has something special about him/her. You may not be the best student in school or the most responsible person at home, but there is something that makes you unique. I think that uniqueness should always be celebrated.

What were the biggest challenges involved in the writing of this play?
It's always challenging for an older person to write for younger people. There is a huge sense of responsibility to get those characters right! Not only is it important to use the

language of young people (without condescending to them), it is also important to write about subjects that resonate with them. I think the secret is to find those issues that are universal. Although I'm certainly no longer a teenager, I can still understand Morgan's sense of succumbing to pressure and the belief that no one notices what makes me special.

What inspired you to become a playwright?
I came to playwriting later than most writers, but I was always a "theatre kid." From the moment I was cast as the Cowardly Lion in *The Wizard of Oz* in the sixth grade, I was hooked! I have acted, directed, and taught for many years. About five years ago, I took a playwriting class just for fun. I loved it and continued to write. I decided to get my MFA in playwriting, and the work I have done at Hollins University has been some of the most rewarding of my life.

Are any characters modeled after real life or historical figures?
The character of Morgan is modeled after my daughter—not that she's a table-setting champion or anything. I saw that she was dealing with a lot of pressures, and I wanted to write something for her so that she would know that I was aware of that. Morgan can be played by either a boy or a girl because I think those pressures are universal. We all know what it feels like to feel like nothing.

Shakespeare gave advice to the players in *Hamlet*; if you could give advice to your cast what would it be?
If you are playing the parents, think of what it is like when your parents disapprove of your choices. How do you picture them? What do they look like when they talk about your shortcomings? What do they sound like? That's what you can base those characters on. If you are playing Morgan,

remember a time when somebody told you that you weren't good enough. That's how Morgan usually feels. But the joy of Morgan is the ability to bounce back and believe in himself/herself. Above all, Morgan is a trouper. The show must go on, and the show should be fun. Have fun!

About the Author

Laura King is a member of the Playwright's Lab at Hollins University. She has had 10-minute plays produced across the country, including her youth plays *The Disappointments, The Dodo Pact, The Crackling Rainbow Comet, How Penny Got Her Pep Back, The Piggy Pit,* and *Tag.* She is the author of the full-length plays *Independence Day at Happy Meadows, The Harmony Baptist Church Ladies Auxiliary Christmas Jubilee, Fallout,* and *Blood Will Out.*

SPEECH & DEBATE

A short drama by
Will Coleman

CAST OF CHARACTERS

KAREN, female, 16, she has a lot on her plate.

MOM, female, 36, unable to work due to pain.

The biggest obstacle to freedom is love.

(Helen's kitchen. Her MOM is sitting down with a washcloth over her eyes.)

(HELEN enters.)

MOM: Is that you?

HELEN: I need to tell you something.

MOM: Come here, sweetie.

(Helen goes to her mother, who hugs her without removing the washcloth.)

HELEN: Oh. Uh, how you feeling?

MOM: Same.

HELEN: You, uh—stayed home again today?

MOM: Hurts to move.

HELEN: Okay. You want a sandwich or something?

MOM: No, no, I ate.

HELEN: I'm gonna make you a sandwich.

(Throughout the following, she makes her mom a sandwich.)

MOM: ...Okay. Thank you. Tell me about it.

HELEN: I need to tell you—

MOM: About class. Debate.

HELEN: Well, I—uh, no, you rest, we can talk about it later.

MOM: Helen.

HELEN: It went fine, okay? A on the paper.

MOM: Number.

HELEN: An A's an A, Mom.

MOM: Since when?

HELEN: 93.

MOM: That's the lowest A.

HELEN: Yep.

MOM: Don't get too many, it can bring the average down.

HELEN: I know, Mom.

MOM: So that's Lit, then you've got Chemistry?

HELEN: Yeah.

MOM: Quiz?

HELEN: Molar mass.

MOM: Uh-oh.

HELEN: I passed.

MOM: Helen

HELEN: Eight out of ten.

MOM: That's a B.

HELEN: It doesn't matter, the quizzes are pass/fail.

MOM: You're not strong enough in Chemistry, I'm sure there's someone who can tutor you.

HELEN: Mom, I have the second highest grade in the class.

(Mom removes her washcloth for the first time.)

MOM: Tenth Grade Chemistry. Should've taken Honors.

HELEN: ...

MOM: Nothing to say?

HELEN: I'm sorry.

(She gives her mom the sandwich.)

(Mom takes a bite, chews, puts the sandwich aside.)

MOM: Thank you, honey.

HELEN: You need to eat.

(Mom puts the washcloth back over her eyes.)

MOM: You wore that to Debate?

HELEN: I'm...I'm not changing clothes for Debate.

MOM: Appearance is important in Debate. You need to be taken seriously.

HELEN: I know.

MOM: Okay.

HELEN: I've got homework.

MOM: We're not done.

HELEN: It's a lot of homework. We can talk about it when you're feeling better.

MOM: I don't feel better.

HELEN: I know.

MOM: What?

HELEN: You don't feel better. You never feel better.

MOM: I have fibro — [fibromyalgia]

HELEN: The doctors don't seem to think so.

MOM: Doctors are idiots.

HELEN: Then why do I have to be one?

MOM: Oh do not start with this again, honey, please. It makes me tired.

HELEN: I'm just not sure I need to be doing all of this.

MOM: This is not the time to have doubts.

HELEN: Sixteen?

MOM: Absolutely. You're lucky. My mother had no plan for me. I just drifted through school, having fun, going out with boys, and now 20 years later, I'm alone and infirm and my daughter doesn't even want to give me the time of day.

HELEN: I appreciate it, I just...

MOM: How was Debate?

HELEN: I — good.

MOM: You ready for Saturday?

HELEN: I don't —

MOM: You're not ready? You've been working so hard!

HELEN: It's not that, I just...

MOM: What?

HELEN: I —

MOM: What?

HELEN: Mom.

(She takes off her washcloth.)

MOM: Don't scare me.

HELEN: I quit Debate.

(Beat.)

(The washcloth goes back on.)

MOM: Oh. Is that all?

HELEN: I didn't go.

MOM: Okay.

HELEN: I don't want to go. I didn't go today. I'm quitting.

MOM: I heard you. I'm gonna take a rest, you can do dinner on your own?

HELEN: You—you don't care about Debate?

MOM: It's your life, darling, you want to quit Debate, then quit it.

HELEN: Okay.

MOM: Okay. You can eat whatever you want.

HELEN: What?

MOM: You know, for dinner.

HELEN: Okay.

MOM: Since you're not going to Debate.

HELEN: What?

MOM: Well, I mean, I guess it doesn't matter what you look like, so eat whatever you want.

HELEN: Oh my god.

MOM: Is that not what you want?

HELEN: Fine. Maybe I will.

MOM: Okay, good.

HELEN: Maybe I'll just go get some burgers.

MOM: Great.

HELEN: And some doughnuts, what is that called? A Luther Vandross? A cheeseburger with doughnuts instead of bread? That sounds amazing, doesn't it?

MOM: Mm-hmm.

HELEN: Maybe I'll invent my own. Something they'll start calling a Helen Poole. Won't that be fun? Maybe an ice cream burrito or something like that.

MOM: Okay.

HELEN: 'Cause I like Tex-Mex.

MOM: Good.

HELEN: Jesus, Mom, what the hell is wrong with you? [Feel free to substitute an alternate expletive for *Jesus*.]

(Washcloth comes off.)

MOM: I am Living, Breathing, Dying for you.

HELEN: Please don't start on this.

MOM: I am in Pain, Helen. All of the time.

HELEN: Yeah, I know. Now. And a few years ago it was Diabetes, Hypothyroidism, Celiac's Disease...

MOM: I'm not discussing this with you.

HELEN: Because the people at Debate need to take me seriously, but you don't.

MOM: I ache, Helen. I can't work because my joints are on fire, and movement makes them flare up. I can't sleep, I can't eat.

HELEN: So I have to suffer with you?

MOM: I suffer for you. The only thing that gets me through the day is thinking of you. You succeeding. You making something better of your life than a dental receptionist raising a child alone.

HELEN: Don't—

MOM: But you. You're so much smarter than me. Prettier than me. I'm sorry I'm tough on you, baby, I really am. I just... I want you to be the best. Is that so bad?

HELEN: No.

MOM: And sometimes, when you don't try your hardest...it hurts my feelings.

HELEN: When? When did I not try my hardest?

MOM: When you quit softball.

HELEN: I hated softball. I wasn't good at it.

MOM: You didn't practice.

HELEN: I'm not—

MOM: If you had practiced, you—

HELEN: I don't—

MOM: You think Tiger Woods—

HELEN: Mom—

MOM: Serena Williams?

HELEN: It's not about you!

MOM: Oh.

HELEN: I quit 'cause I didn't like it. And I quit Debate, okay? I just drove around until enough time had passed and came home. And I'm sorry. I'm sorry about that, but only sort of, because I hate talking in front of people and I'm not going to become a lawyer, and I hate Debate and Mr. Fernikan, and I'm not going back.

MOM: Okay.

HELEN: What?

MOM: I love you.

HELEN: Don't do this.

MOM: If you need money for a burger or something, just take it out of my purse.

HELEN: Mom.

MOM: I'm really tired, honey.

HELEN: I —

MOM: You think you could run some cold water on this?

HELEN: If you eat that sandwich.

MOM: Helen, I'll —

HELEN: Eat it, and I'll get it.

MOM: I —

HELEN: Mom.

(Mom takes a bite of the sandwich.)

(She hands Helen the washcloth.)

(Helen walks offstage.)

(She comes back, and places the washcloth on her mom's face.)

(She kisses her forehead.)

(She continues eating.)

(Helen exits.)

(End of play.)

The Author Speaks

What inspired you to write this play?
In a class we were tasked with writing a ten-minute play about parental pressure. The idea of the unsatisfied parent, who expects more, even when the child excels, immediately jumped to mind as perhaps something that might not get a lot of attention. Likewise, the mother must be dealing with pressure of her own, so that kind of came out of that.

Have you dealt with the same theme in other works that you have written?
I've dealt with the complicated relationships between parents and children before, and the pressure anyone puts on themselves for the people that we love, but I feel that's fairly universal.

What writers have had the most profound effect on your style?
I'm not really sure if this is apparent in this particular work, but Caryl Churchill is my favorite playwright. I love her sense of the theatrical, all of her plays have something in them that can only be done, or at least work best, on stage, as opposed to any other medium. Her plays tend to be very dark, but with a lot of humor and whimsical elements in them, and that's something that I try to keep in my own work.

What do you hope to achieve with this work?
A conversation between parents and their child. I think that all theatre is about the conversations we can inspire, and if a parent can recognize behavior or better understand the pressures of modern day teenagers, then that would be my wildest hope.

What were the biggest challenges involved in the writing of this play?
It was important to me to make both the characters relatable and true to life. I wouldn't want any teenager to think that Helen didn't sound like a 16-year-old, for example, because if you can't get a voice right, then you lose the audience immediately.

What are the most common mistakes that occur in productions of your work?
I've had very few productions and don't get a chance to see the ones I do have, so I don't really have a good conception of any "mistakes." That being said I try to give lots of room in my work for directors, actors, and designers to be creative, so if something is quite different from the way I originally conceived it, I wouldn't call it a mistake.

What inspired you to become a playwright?
Reading and seeing plays. I've always been writing, and I still write prose, but my real discovery of theatre in high school inspired me to try writing plays as well, and I've never really stopped since then.

Are any characters modeled after real life or historical figures?
Not specifically, although I definitely knew some students in high school who seemed to be best at everything, sports, academics, popular, etc., but they still struggled with the expectations of their parents.

About the Author

Will Coleman is a playwright and director living in Chicago. His play *Helvetica* won the 2015 Getchell new play award from SETC and was produced at Mill Mountain Theatre in January 2015. His ten-minute play, *Spooky Action at a Distance* premiered at Tesseract Theatre in St. Louis in November 2014, and his musical *Zombie Boyfriend!* (co-written with Chandler Davis) premiered in 2011, and will be produced by Wheelhouse in 2016. He is currently an MFA candidate at the Playwright's Lab at Hollins University.

SWEET DREAMS

A short comedy by
Wendy-Marie Martin

CAST OF CHARACTERS

JORDAN, a 16-year-old super student whose academic goals are beginning to take their toll. She is a straight-laced good girl.

FAYE, an extravagant female teen fairy usually decked out in some funky, crazy outfit and fully accessorized with as much glitz and glitter as possible. (Most people mistake her for a high fashion model.) She is a boisterous diva who knows how to have fun.

(Lights up on JORDAN, balancing an unbelievably high stack of books. She trips and the books fall to the floor.)

JORDAN: Oh come on. Give me a break!

(Jordan begins to pick up the books as FAYE enters dressed like she's ready for a fashion show in Paris.)

FAYE: You called?

JORDAN: Excuse me? Who are you?

FAYE: Faye — your B.F.F. Fairy. Just in time, too, by the looks of things —

(Faye helps Jordan pick up books.)

JORDAN: My B.F. what?

FAYE: Fairy. I believe you requested someone to... *(Looking through her notes:)* ..."give you a break."

JORDAN: *(Rubbing her eyes:)* I really did stay up too late last night. *(Blinking a few times:)* You're still here.

FAYE: B.F.F. Fairies don't leave until the job is done. It's in our contract.

JORDAN: I'm sorry, I have no idea what a B...F...F Fairy is —

FAYE: Seriously? What are they teaching you in school?

(Faye assesses Jordan and makes a few notes.)

JORDAN: *(Shaking her head to clear it:)* I've finally lost it. *(Deep breath.)* Focus, Jordan. You need to study.

(Jordan takes a stack of books back to a desk. Faye follows her.)

FAYE: Study? On a Saturday morning? You should be hanging out with your friends or...

(Takes Jordan's hand.)

...getting a desperately needed manicure.

JORDAN: Hey—

FAYE: Or at least sleeping the day away like a normal teenager—

JORDAN: Sleep? Are you kidding me? I've got SATs coming up. I have to pass with at least a 2300 or I can forget Harvard. Wait, why am I talking to a hallucination?

FAYE: First of all, I'm not a hallucination. Rude. Secondly... you're the one who asked for a break, remember? That's why I'm here in the first place. And I've got a bunch of other people to help today, so if we could move this along, I would appreciate it. Liliana is NOT going to beat my high score again this month.

JORDAN: High score?

FAYE: Complicated fairy stuff. You wouldn't understand. Now back to you...if all this SAT stuff and Harvard, or whatever, is stressing you out so much why don't you just forget about it?

JORDAN: Forget Harvard, are you insane?

FAYE: There are lots of other schools you can go—

JORDAN: No there's not—

FAYE: Sure there are, silly. There's like thousands of colleges, especially with all the junior colleges—

JORDAN: Junior college? No way. There's only one school for me. Harvard. *(Beat.)* Stop talking to the air, Jordan. You're losing it. Study.

(Jordan puts on a set of headphones and opens a book. Faye leans next to her, trying to hear her jam.)

FAYE: That is not...classical music.

JORDAN: Excuse me?

FAYE: Old people listen to classical music. You should be listening to...

> *(Faye snaps her fingers and the library is transformed into a disco. [If this isn't possible, Faye can sing something a cappella instead as she jumps up on the table and dances wildly.])*

> *(Jordan tries to continue studying, but Faye makes it very difficult. Jordan packs her books up and gets ready to leave. Faye finally notices and stops.)*

Hey...heyheyheyhey. Where are you going?

JORDAN: Somewhere I can study—and listen to my music, which I happen to like, thank you very much—in peace.

FAYE: But I can't leave you alone until I give you a break. Those are the rules.

JORDAN: My family has been going to Harvard since the first class graduated in 1642—

FAYE: Yeah? Well my family has been in the fairy business longer than that, and we don't quit until the job is done. Now I've got a quota to fill, if you don't mind, so I'd like to finish your assessment.

JORDAN: Look, I know you're probably a figment of my imagination conjured from a mixture of stress and sleep deprivation, but I've got exactly one week left to study. If I don't ace my SATs I'll be branded a failure—

FAYE: Ha. I've got it! You need a sleep-out.

JORDAN: A sleep-what?

FAYE: A sleep-out. *(Beat.)* A sleep-out? It's so clear, I can't believe I didn't think of it before.

JORDAN: I have no idea what you're talking about.

FAYE: A sleep-out is like a time-out but in bed. Asleep.

JORDAN: I don't know. I don't think—

FAYE: Look, you summoned me, remember? Now I don't want to be rude, but I've got a lot of other stressed out overachievers to help, so you're going to have to pick your poison. Now do you want some sleep or not?

JORDAN: A nap would be pretty amazing, but...what about studying?

FAYE: The books will still be here when you wake up. Only difference is...you'll actually be able to keep your eyes open while you read them.

(Beat.)

JORDAN: Ooooh...kay.

FAYE: Okay? You mean it?

JORDAN: Yes, just...do it quick before I change my mind!

(Faye blows fairy dust in Jordan's direction as a bed appears. Faye tucks Jordan in and sets the alarm, as Jordan falls asleep.)

FAYE: Sweet dreams.

(Jordan falls asleep immediately.)

Few days of sleep should help your stress levels. And don't you dare think about what you've done while you're sleeping, young lady! I'll just wait to make sure you're in REM and then...

(Faye starts to fade, then crawls in with her feet in Jordan's face and starts to snore. The alarm goes off. Jordan opens her eyes, sits up and screams, which wakes up Faye.)

What, whatwahtwhatwhatwhat?

JORDAN: You're...you're... What time is it?

FAYE: Uh... One hundred o'clock —

JORDAN: What?

FAYE: Or 10. Yeah. That makes sense. It's probably 10 o'clock.

JORDAN: Ten o'clock? ...what day?

FAYE: Uhmmmm....looks like it's...Friday. Wait —

JORDAN: FRIDAY? No, nononononono that's not possible. Tomorrow is my test day, and I just lost a week of study time? What was I thinking?

FAYE: Friday??!! Liliana is going to be days ahead of me now! I'm never going to be the top fairy. Ever!

FAYE: I can't even handle a simple sleep-out. I mean, look at you! You're more stressed now than you were before.

JORDAN: ...actually, I feel pretty good —

FAYE: Clearly you're just saying that to make me feel better. I mean, look at you.

JORDAN: No, it's true... I feel good. Really, really good. So...rested. And clear. *(Beat.)* Wait. Ask me a question. Any question.

FAYE: Like what?

JORDAN: The projected sales volume of a video game disc is given by function $s(p)$ equals 3,000 over $2p$ + a where s is the number of discs sold, in thousands; p is the price per disc, in dollars; and a is constant —

FAYE: Huh?

JORDAN: If according to the projections, 100,000 discs are sold at 10 dollars per disc, how many discs will be sold at 20 dollars per disc?

FAYE: I have no idea. Why are you asking me?

JORDAN: Sixty-thousand! S(20) equals three thousand over 2(20) plus 10, which equals sixty. Oh my god... The answers. They're so clear in my head. This is amazing. I...I had no idea.

FAYE: Yeah, sleep is pretty cool stuff.

JORDAN: I have to tell my parents. I have to tell my friends. My best friend, Jessica, hasn't sleep a full night since freshman year. Wait. Even better. I could give them all sleep-outs —

FAYE: Too bad you're not a fairy —

JORDAN: True, but... *(An idea is forming:)* ...you get points or something for each person you help, right?

FAYE: Sort of. They track our fairy dust —

JORDAN: Perfect. What if I could help you help a whole bunch more people? Increase your productivity levels by like...

(Pulls out a calculator.)

Sixty-two and a half percent.

FAYE: That would be amazing! Man I'd love to see the look on Liliana's face when my name is on top of the scoreboard. Problem, though... You're still not a fairy.

JORDAN: Good thing I know a super smart one that can teach me her tricks, right?

FAYE: Huh?

JORDAN: A nice, good fairy who could teach me how to give a sleep-out? ...And get her ratings up at the same time...? Beat Liliana and become top score...

FAYE: Oh... Oooooh. You mean I could teach you!

JORDAN: SAT scores would skyrocket. Just think —

FAYE: Yeah...wait. No! No. Nononon00000. That's not possible. Only fairies —

JORDAN: How hard can it be?

FAYE: Well, first you'd have to find fairy dust and then...you'd have to plant the idea in someone's mind and...sprinkle the dust and...set the alarm. It's very complicated, you know...

(Jordan follows her directions, ending by sprinkling some fairy dust on Faye's head.)

JORDAN: Time for a sleep-out, Faye —

FAYE: Very funny, you can't —

(Faye falls asleep immediately.)

JORDAN: Oh but I can!

(Pours fairy dust into a small test tube.)

Time for us both to win, my friend. Harvard here I come.

(Holds up the test tube triumphantly.)

Sleep for all!

(Jordan tucks Faye in.)

When you wake up, your name will be at the top of the scoreboard. Promise. Sweet dreams!

(Jordan exits as lights fade.)

(End of play.)

The Author Speaks

Was the structure or other elements of the play influenced by any other work?
Faye is a modern fairy with elements of classic, spunky fairies like Thumbelina and Tinkerbell mixed in with a touch of Lady Gaga. My goal was to give high school performers something crazy to play with so they could go all out with this character and think outside of the box. I had this high-fashion model vision in my brain, which I thought would be so much fun for a young costume designer to play with and give the actress playing Faye an opportunity to work together with her director and costume designer to create unique, crazy character. Also, I wanted Jordan to have the opportunity to let go of her stress for a moment in time and be free.

Have you dealt with the same theme in other works that you have written?
I enjoy writing female characters that are bold and strong and not afraid to break the rules. Both Faye and Jordan are ambitious and determined, but need each other to reach their goals. They also both have many opportunities for physical comedy and big character choices, which I love watching female teen actors discover.

What writers have had the most profound effect on your style?
As far as comedies are concerned, I often find Christopher Durang's campy, outrageous approach to humor in the back of my mind while I'm writing. Also Jeff Goode's vigilante comic stylings remind me that nothing is really too silly to try.

What do you hope to achieve with this work?

I hope that my play gives high school actors the opportunity to have fun while exploring a serious topic...sleep deprivation. I hope it makes overachievers realize the power of sleep and realize how important it is for them to give themselves a break every now and then. It also gives teenagers on the brink of adulthood permission to be children again and go to a silly place. I would really love it if the actors playing Faye and Jordan have so much fun with these characters that they find themselves releasing any built up stress during the performances.

What were the biggest challenges involved in the writing of this play?

I kept finding myself wanting to apologize for the silliness of this play while I was writing it. I was afraid young actors wouldn't want to play a fairy or find the concept of a B.F.F. fairy childish. But the actresses that have played Faye so far said they thought it was a blast. Once I had that feedback, I feel much freer to go further with the concept and make it even sillier, which I think really served the play.

What are the most common mistakes that occur in productions of your work?

I tend to write a quick paced tempo in my comedies and find sometimes actors like to milk lines too much. Pace is everything, so I prefer pauses or decelerations be earned. If it gets too heavy, the pace slows down and the comedy is sometimes lost.

What inspired you to become a playwright?

My high school drama teacher was a playwright and made us write our own monologues and scenes in acting class, so playwriting was a natural extension of theatremaking for me. I started as an actor and then moved into directing and at one point realized that playwriting is the culmination of everything I love to do. Playwriting allows me to act all the roles and direct the scenes in my mind as a write without every having to get on stage.

How did you research the subject?

I spoke to high school students experiencing SAT stress and surfed the web for SAT test statistics. I also found an SAT practice test for sample questions to know what Jordan was up against. My daughter was preparing to take the SAT for the first time while I was writing the play, so she was very helpful, too!

Are any characters modeled after real life or historical figures?

I worked with a cast of extremely smart, ambitious young women in the play I directed at Nipomo High School. They were in a ton of AP classes with big goals for their academic future. I would say Jordan is a combination of many of their personality traits. My vision for Faye was based on a Lady Gaga, high-fashion type of young lady mixed with a Lucille Ball-esque comic.

Shakespeare gave advice to the players in *Hamlet*; if you could give advice to your cast what would it be?

Have fun and push the characters to the limit. Fairyland is whatever you envision (together with your director) and can be as crazy as you like. I think the bigger and bolder Faye can be, the more it will lead Jordan on a larger journey.

How was the first production different from the vision that you created in your mind?
I actually did rewrites after the first reading/production (and feedback from our publisher!) to give Jordan more power over her situation, which took the play to a new level. Originally I had Faye controlling Jordan's situation far too much, but now Jordan actually takes the reins in the end and makes her own decision to embrace the power of the sleep-out. The rewrites helped make Jordan more active and in control of her own destiny.

About the Author

Wendy-Marie Martin earned an MFA in Playwriting from the Hollins Playwright's Lab at Hollins University and holds a BFA in Acting as well. She's written, directed & produced intimate theatre projects in the U.S. and Europe. Her short plays have been produced in Germany, The Netherlands, Australia, and the U.S. She is also creator and Executive Producer of The Red Eye 10s Play Festival, a nationwide festival of original shorts. Wendy-Marie is a member of the Dramatists Guild, TCG, and Playwrights' Center, and is also the 2015-16 Resident Playwright at Tesseract Theatre Company in St. Louis.

THE SUMMONING SKY

A short drama by
Marshall N. Opie

CAST OF CHARACTERS
RUTHIE, a caring, concerned mom.
LUCY, Ruthie's mother-in-law.
SAM, Ruthie's 14-year-old son.

SETTING
A large, open-spaced living room/den/library area.

(LUCY dusts framed family photos. RUTHIE and SAM enter the front door of the house. Ruthie is carrying a package wrapped in brown parcel paper.)

(Sam walks to a space in the room that is all his own. There are lots of books in his space that he has systematically organized.)

(Ruthie removes an urn from the package.)

LUCY: *(Pointing to the urn in Ruthie's hands:)* So how much, Ruthie? How much did you pay for that—that—

RUTHIE: It's an urn, Lucy. Isn't it handsome? And it was cheaper than a casket.

LUCY: And smaller than a bread basket. Whoop de doo. I still don't want the ashes in the house. They give me the heebie-jeebies. *(Handing Ruthie an envelope:)* You have mail here from Sam's school—

RUTHIE: *(Opening and reading the letter:)* I wonder what now.

SAM: Where's my book?

RUTHIE: Which book?

SAM: My book that was here.

LUCY: Don't get upset, Sam. I borrowed it.

(She picks up the book from the table and gives it to Sam.)

I'm sorry.

(Sam becomes lost in the book.)

RUTHIE: Why would you touch his book? You know how he is about people messing with his stuff.

SAM: That's okay, Grandma.

LUCY: I wanted to know what he was reading. What was in the envelope?

RUTHIE: Sam's progress report. The grades aren't looking good.

LUCY: How can that be? He's always studying.

RUTHIE: Yeah, reading and studying everything but his school work. I'm going to have him tested.

LUCY: Tested? His father died not even a month ago. Give him time.

RUTHIE: "Give him time," you've been saying that for quite a while. I'm concerned. I'd like Sam to make at least one good friend.

LUCY: Sam has plenty of friends. Look at all his friends that came to the funeral. Right, Sam?

SAM: I want to go for a walk.

RUTHIE: A walk? No. You have school work to do.

SAM: I just want to walk in the woods and peer through the branches of the trees and look at the sky.

RUTHIE: Not now, Sam.

SAM: Dad was my friend. If he were here, he would say, "Let's go for a walk, Bud," and he and I would just go out back and walk in the woods. Why can't I go for a walk?

LUCY: You miss those walks, don't you?

SAM: I went for a walk yesterday.

RUTHIE: And that's why you're not going for a walk today.

SAM: I'm talking to Grandma.

LUCY: Don't talk to your mother that way.

SAM: The trees didn't seem to be happy.

RUTHIE: That's all right. He won't be going for a walk for a while.

LUCY: Maybe the trees weren't happy because they miss your father.

SAM: They didn't seem as tall as they used to.

(Ruthie opens a box containing ashes and begins transferring the ashes from the box to the urn.)

LUCY: Be careful, Ruthie. Can't you do that outside? I don't want any of those ashes falling on the floor.

RUTHIE: They're falling right into the urn, see?

LUCY: Maybe the trees aren't as tall because you're not as short as you used to be.

SAM: I guess. Dad and I called the woods our avatar jungle.

RUTHIE: Avatar jungle?

LUCY: It's in the book.

RUTHIE: Oh —

LUCY: Please be careful.

RUTHIE: I've got this.

LUCY: I'm curious, Sam. What did you and your dad talk about when you went on your walks?

SAM: Different things.

LUCY: Did you talk about the book?

SAM: Sometimes we did, and other books. Sometimes I didn't want to talk at all, and neither did he. We had a special way of communicating to each other without talking. I knew when he was happy, and I knew when he was sad. Our walks always made us happy.

LUCY: What are you doing now, Ruthie?

SAM: Are you listening, Grandma?

RUTHIE: Finding a place for Tom's ashes.

LUCY: Yes, I'm listening. I'm sorry. One second, Sam. Now, Ruthie, I wish you would listen to me. I'd really prefer that we purchase a place to put those ashes in the cemetery.

RUTHIE: We can't afford it, and I prefer to have them here.

SAM: When I was walking in the woods yesterday, I heard his voice.

LUCY: Whose voice?

SAM: Dad's voice. I looked up at the sky, and it was summoning me...

RUTHIE: What are you talking about?

LUCY: Shh. Listen. That's where I went wrong as a parent. The sky was summoning you?

SAM: Yes, in a voice like Dad's, calling me to fly like an avatar.

RUTHIE: Avatars don't fly; they leap.

SAM: How would you know that?

RUTHIE: I read it in your book.

SAM: *(Angry:)* My book?

RUTHIE: I can't read your book, but it's okay with you if your grandmother does?

SAM: No.

(Sam begins to hum, "I'll Fly Away.")

RUTHIE: Please don't hum that.

SAM: It's Dad's song.

RUTHIE: No. That's your grandmother's song that she insisted be sung at the funeral.

SAM: I like it.

LUCY: I do too.

(Lucy begins singing, "I'll Fly Away.")

RUTHIE: Well I don't.

(Sam joins in singing with Lucy.)

Stop it. The both of you stop. They are going to hold you back a year in school!

(Beat.)

Stop it!

(After a moment of awkward silence, Lucy walks and picks up a photograph of a man – it's her son. Ruthie returns to searching for a place for the urn.)

SAM: Hold me back?

RUTHIE: Yes, if your grades don't improve.

SAM: I want to move on with my class.

RUTHIE: You're going to have to stop your daydreaming.

(Again, awkward silence. Sam picks up his book. Lucy embraces the photograph.)

SAM: I'll try.

RUTHIE: You're going to have to do better than try.

(Ruthie places the urn down.)

LUCY: Not there.

RUTHIE: Then where?

LUCY: I don't know. Why must you hold on to them?

RUTHIE: If you can hold on to old photographs, why can't I hold on to my husband's ashes?

SAM: Dad wouldn't take me to see the movie unless I read the novel first.

RUTHIE: What are you talking about now?

SAM: I thought the movie, *Avatar*, was inspired by the cartoon, *Avatar: The Last Airbender*, but Dad thought it was inspired by this novel, *Songs from the Stars*. I think he was right.

RUTHIE: Focus, Sam. You can't help yourself, can you?

SAM: I am focused. Can't you hear him?

LUCY: Hear who?

SAM: Dad.

RUTHIE: No.

SAM: It's like the book. Humans can receive messages from other worlds with advanced civilizations through songs. I can hear him, singing "I'll Fly Away." And now he's saying he's leaving, but he'll always be here for us, and he's sorry. He's very sorry. He does love us all, and he's sorry.

RUTHIE: Sam, come here, baby. Please. Can I hold you?

SAM: You don't believe me, do you? Do you? You think it's all my imagination.

RUTHIE: No—

SAM: I'm not crazy, and neither was Dad. You don't understand us.

RUTHIE: I'm trying to understand.

SAM: You think I'm sick like you thought Dad was sick.

RUTHIE: Sick? You're not sick.

SAM: Then what am I?

RUTHIE: You are brilliant.

SAM: Brilliant?

RUTHIE: Yes. Like your father, like Mozart, and like Einstein: you are brilliant.

SAM: *(Beat.)* You don't believe me that I can hear him, do you?

RUTHIE: It doesn't matter if I believe.

SAM: Do you believe me, Grandma?

LUCY: I believe in you, baby.

SAM: But you don't believe me.

LUCY: I want to believe —

(Sam walks towards his father's urn and picks it up.)

RUTHIE: What are you doing?

SAM: In the movie, the humans thought that the aliens were primitive and ignorant.

LUCY: Sam —

SAM: The aliens came from an ancient, rich culture that honored nature and the creator of life.

(Sam turns to take the urn out the front door.)

RUTHIE: Sam, what are you doing?

SAM: I'm listening to Dad. You don't hear him.

RUTHIE: Sam, give me that —!

LUCY: Sam, your dad wouldn't tell you to do something wrong.

(Ruthie tries to take the urn from Sam.)

Let it go.

SAM: No.

RUTHIE: Let it go —

SAM: No.

LUCY: Sam — let it —

(In the struggle for the urn, the urn falls to the floor and the ashes fall out as well.)

SAM AND RUTHIE: NO...!

LUCY: *(Gasping:)* No — *(Beat.)* Tom.

RUTHIE: What are you doing, Sam?

SAM: I'm releasing him. Dad says he wants to be released into the woods.

LUCY: What are you talking about, Tom — *(She exhales.)* Sam — Baby.

RUTHIE: Your dad wants to be released into the woods?

(Gently scooping up the ashes into the urn.)

SAM: Yes.

(He bends down with his mother and helps her to place the ashes into the urn.)

He wants me to climb into the trees and let his ashes fly into the air.

RUTHIE: Just like that?

SAM: Just like that.

RUTHIE: Is that what you want?

SAM: Yes.

RUTHIE: What about you, Lucy?

LUCY: If you are taking them out the house, I'm happy. Take 'em up in a tree and make the trees happy. Just please, Dear Lord, take 'em out of here. If that's what Sam says Tom wants, then that's what we should do.

RUTHIE: Okay. We will let the ashes fly away.

SAM: We will have a memorial service just like you wanted, Mom. Just the three of us.

RUTHIE: Just the three of us.

(Ruthie and Sam continue to gently clean up the ashes. Lucy sings, "I'll Fly Away." Sam joins in and then Ruthie. The three sing joyously.)

(Lights dim. End of play.)

The Author Speaks

What inspired you to write this play?
The play was written in response to an assignment in a class I took entitled Theatre for Young Audiences and in hopes of being part of an anthology of 10-minute plays entitled *Great Expectations.* The true source of the material came as I reflected on the challenges I had in engaging a particular student I taught the previous school year. This student, I strongly feel, was extremely bright despite his poor performance in my class and in most of the classes he took. Truly this student was the initial prototype for Sam, the daydreamer in the play *The Summoning Sky.* Since I am one who still enjoys occasional daydreaming, my initial intent was to create Sam as a pure daydreamer, poet, and genius in the making. Sam, like his prototype, I never once considered to have a "disability." To me, Sam and his prototype are filled with ability. To me the challenge in writing this play, as often is the challenge in teaching any child, was finding the right hook to engage, guide, and direct Sam to pursue a meaningful goal and resolve the problems in the world in which he resides.

Was the structure or other elements of the play influenced by any other work?
I really can't say. The only influence was the thought that I wanted this piece to be a total experiment, "experimental theatre." This was my thought, and this was my goal. The play would weave the poetry of Sam's thoughts intertwined with the lyrical, rhythmic nature of Ruthie and Lucy's "working-class" dialogues. I explored this type of effort before in other plays that I had written and experienced some degree of success.

Have you dealt with the same theme in other works that you have written?
Faith, love, family, community...in some form or fashion every play I have written touches on these topics. Faith upholds, encourages, and sustains love. True love overcomes weakness, ignorance, sickness, and death. True love strengthens individuals and families. Strong families tend to build strong communities. Many of these themes are touched on within this play. These are themes I find myself pursuing and writing about.

What writers have had the most profound effect on your style?
I would say that I'm pretty eclectic and that I haven't found one particular writer within any genre that I profess to follow or model myself after. There are many playwrights with whose accomplishments I am impressed, such as Lorraine Hansberry, August Wilson, William Shakespeare, Arthur Miller, Rodgers and Hammerstein, Sophocles, and Bertolt Brecht, to name a few from the top of my head. I could add Langston Hughes to the list, but if I were to add Hughes to the list it would not be because of the influence of his writings as a playwright but as a poet.

If I were to choose a favorite poet, hands-down it would be Langston Hughes because of the unique and humorous way in which he captures witty language of everyday people. I would also choose Langston Hughes because as a writer he was greatly influenced by the sounds of blues, be-bop, gospel, and jazz music — which are all true sources of inspiration for me as well.

What do you hope to achieve with this work?
I would like to be known as a writer. Not a black writer, not a writer for young audiences, not a writer for special populations, but simply a writer. As a writer, I would like to persuade readers and future leaders, who may also be writers, to join me in actualizing some of the themes found within this work in order that no child be left behind and no adult feel like they are all alone.

What were the biggest challenges involved in the writing of this play?
I guess the biggest challenge in writing this play was making the choice to write a play with a beginning, middle and end. That sounds simple enough, but it wasn't, because my initial choice was to "experiment." I enjoyed the initial experiment. I knew what I was saying; I knew what, in particular, Sam was thinking; and I felt strongly that this play was important. However, others, as they perceived the potential impact of the play, did not fully understand the experiment, Sam, or the ending. As playwright and advocate, I felt the tough choices I made to compromise "the experiment" I paid off in the end and were essential in strengthening and empowering Sam's voice.

What are the most common mistakes that occur in productions of your work?
The most common mistake is when a director chooses to ignore parentheticals, stage directions, and even simple punctuation. Because music and lyrics are important to me, lines and words should be said melodically and with rhythm and silence and beats that should not be ignored.

What inspired you to become a playwright?
I was inspired to become a playwright through a song that I wrote. One day, I was playing the song on the piano and suddenly characters began speaking and jumping off the keys. I call that day *my fiery burning bush experience.*

How did you research the subject?
I researched the subject matter through observation, interviews, the Internet, books, and videos. As I've stated, Sam was created initially as a "regular" child who enjoyed daydreaming. Overtime, as the script developed, Sam's "abilities" became stigmatized as a disability. Within the script, I chose not to classify or label Sam with any diagnosis. The reason for this is that it became cloudy to me in my research what is the "politically correct" name for his diagnosis. Once it was clear to me that Sam's condition was political, I was motivated to write and tell his story even the more.

Shakespeare gave advice to the players in *Hamlet*; if you could give advice to your cast what would it be?
I think it is important for actors to remember that a play is a "play," therefore, it is essential that they have fun. One word of caution: though this is a fictional play, the characters are very real, and I hope that the actors, as they enjoy the roles, would also respect the lives that each character represents.

About the Author

Marshall Opie, Artistic Director and Founder of ROLL ON! Productions, LLC (ROLL ON!), obtained his Bachelor of Science degree in mathematics with a minor in civil engineering from Howard University. Since his undergraduate experience, Marshall has gained over 10 years of corporate management experience and well over 25 years of experience teaching, serving and supporting urban schools, churches, and inner-city families throughout the Washington, DC, Metropolitan area, and has written, directed, and produced numerous plays. Marshall was a recipient of National Theatre's New Playwright Grant Award for his first play, entitled **Roll On!** — a drama with music — the brainchild of ROLL ON!, the production company. Through ROLL ON!, Marshall has produced several theatrical plays with acclaimed national and international performing artists including Tony Award Winner Melba Moore, Stellar Nominee Shirley Murdock, and Grammy Award Winners Michael and Regina Winans. Marshall is completing his M.F.A. in Playwriting at Hollins University.

THE DANCE WE DO

A short dramedy by
Anne G'Fellers-Mason

CAST OF CHARACTERS

BECCA, female, 17 years old. High school senior, talented dancer, haunted by her family's legacy and the memory of her brother's and sister's many scholarly achievements.

BRIDGET, female, early 20s. Becca's older sister, currently away in college, views achievement as a competition. She appears as a memory in the play.

BRIAN, male, early 20s. Becca's older brother, currently away in college, views achievement as a competition. He appears as a memory in the play.

AMY, female, 17 years old. High school senior, talented dancer, outgoing and outspoken, one of Becca's good friends.

SETTING

The quad or open outside area of a high school.

(BECCA sits in an open space, a large book spread across her lap. Her backpack, extremely overstuffed, sits beside her. BRIDGET and BRIAN sit behind her, their backs to her.)

(Becca works on a problem, muttering to herself and chewing on the end of her pencil.)

BRIDGET: Wrong.

(Becca erases and tries again.)

BRIAN: So wrong.

(Becca erases, frustration mounting.)

(AMY enters. She's obviously come from dance practice. She is not aware of Bridget and Brian. Becca and Amy make eye contact, there is obvious tension.)

AMY: Hi.

BECCA: *(Weakly:)* Hey.

(Amy sits, finding something to keep herself occupied. Becca returns to her math. After a moment...)

BRIDGET: Not even close.

BRIAN: Man, you are bad at this. Do you even understand how math works?

(Becca erases furiously.)

AMY: That our Precalc homework?

BECCA: *(Preoccupied:)* Extra credit.

AMY: It's a little early in the year for extra credit, don't ya think?

BECCA: I need to keep my average up.

AMY: Becca, it's still August.

BECCA: I'm trying to work, Amy —

AMY: *(Obviously hurt:)* Sorry.

(Becca returns to the problem and writes a new answer.)

BRIDGET: Still wrong. You know, I took Advanced Placement Calculus as a junior, not *Precalculus.*

BRIAN: I took Advanced Placement Calculus as a sophomore, not a junior.

BRIDGET: I got a 2380 on my SAT.

BRIAN: 2385.

BRIDGET AND BRIAN: What did you get, Becca?

(Bridget and Brian exchange a knowing look. Becca grows increasingly frustrated as they continue.)

BRIAN: *(Whispering:)* You're doing it all wrong.

BRIDGET: I never erased a problem, not once. I won the Math Bowl two years in a row.

BRIAN: All wrong.

BRIDGET: Aw, and you're making a mess of your paper, how unfastidious of you.

BRIAN: That means messy. Synonym bedraggled, antonym tidy. 2385, what, what!

BRIDGET: You always were the messiest —

BRIAN: — the smallest —

BRIDGET: — the weakest —

BRIAN: — and definitely NOT the smartest of the Donalson kids. *(To Bridget:)* And I was Math Bowl champ three years in a row, so, chew on that.

(Bridget gives him an incredulous look.)

(Back to Becca:) Mom and Dad were so proud.

BRIDGET: Proud of us, proud of the older siblings.

(They continue to chant their last two lines. Becca erases and erases until there's a hole in her paper.)

BECCA: *(To Bridget and Brian:)* Shut up! Shut up!

AMY: Excuse me?!

BECCA: What—

AMY: Are you mad at me?!

BECCA: No, I, that wasn't—

AMY: Listen, you're weirding me out, Becca. We've barely spoken since school started. Are you avoiding me?

BECCA: I'm not—

AMY: You know, dance team auditions are tomorrow and you haven't been to any of the warm up practices. You're trying out, right?

(Becca tries to speak, but nothing comes out.)

I don't get it. This is your Senior year, and you're not gonna dance? You could get scholarships.

BRIDGET: Major in dance, really? I played oboe, but you don't see me majoring in that. But you *will* see me using my Rhodes scholarship to change the world.

BRIAN: I ate 20 hot dogs in 10 minutes, maybe I should've applied for a scholarship in that instead of accepting my full ride to MIT?

(Bridget and Brian laugh.)

AMY: I thought that's what you wanted. That's what you said you wanted — back when we talked.

BECCA: I —

BRIDGET: Mom and Dad are so proud, proud of US.

BRIAN: They're proud of US.

(Bridget and Brian continue to chant their last two lines.)

BECCA: Stop it and let me think!

(Bridget and Brian fall silent.)

AMY: What is going on? Why are you freaking out?

BECCA: I'm not. I'm fine.

(Amy's not buying it. She stands and pulls a reluctant Becca to her feet.)

AMY: Come on, get up!

BECCA: What are you doing?

AMY: We're gonna dance this out, whatever it is.

BECCA: Amy —

AMY: You did it to me last year after the Brad fiasco. Turnabout is fair play, Donalson. Come on, dance it out! What is it? What's wrong?

(Amy keeps Becca moving, all the while asking her "what's wrong" in different ways over and over.)

BECCA: *(Exploding:)* It's my senior year and my SAT score sucks! I haven't filled out any college apps, and there's no way I'm gonna be a Rhodes Scholar, or get into M-I-freaking-T! I'll be banished from the family, but that's okay since I'm obviously such a disappointment to the Donalson family!

(Becca takes a deep breath, relieved to have finally said it.)

AMY: Your parents come to every performance. Any time you dance, they're there.

BECCA: It's my *only* extracurricular. They HAVE to come.

AMY: *(Pointedly:)* No, they don't.

BECCA: I just—I thought once Brian and Bridget graduated, I'd have room to breathe. But I hear their voices, all the time, picking at me like they used to. Mom and Dad never told 'em to stop. I wish they would've. Maybe they thought it was a big joke, and I was in on it. I don't know. But it's uh, it's the dance we do.

(Amy nods, taking a moment to find the words.)

AMY: Okay, so your siblings did amazing, brainy things, but could either of them dance?

BECCA: No. Brian looked like a chicken. He'd stick his neck out like this.

(She demonstrates.)

BRIAN: Hey, girls were into it.

BRIDGET: What girls?

BECCA: And Bridget, she'd stand in the corner and do this weird kind of bob thing.

AMY: Oh yeah, the awkward corner bob.

BRIAN: Ha!

BRIDGET: It was a statement of nonconformity!

AMY AND BECCA: So awkward.

(They laugh, long and hard. Once the giggles have subsided, Becca takes a deep, cleansing breath.)

BECCA: *(Reciting proudly:)* "We dance to keep the world at bay—"

AMY: *(With passion:)* "—to scare the darkness away—"

BECCA and AMY: *(Really getting into it:)* "—to stand up to the world and say, You—You Can Dance If You Want To."

BECCA: It's a pretty awesome team mantra.

AMY: It's the best team mantra.

(Amy holds out her hand and Becca takes it, squeezing it reassuringly.)

(A horn honks.)

That's my ride. I'll see you in class, right, where you'll talk to me?

BECCA: Yeah, of course. See ya tomorrow.

AMY: And I'll see you at tryouts, after, right?

BECCA: *(Firmly:)* Yes.

(The horn honks a second time.)

AMY: I'm coming!

(Amy leaves with a dramatic flourish, and Becca laughs. She looks back to her math work, but puts it aside. She pulls her phone out of her bag and holds it.)

BECCA: "To stand up to the world and say, You—You Can Dance If You Want To."

(Becca puts headphones in her ears and listens to music on her phone. What starts as a slow tapping of feet turns into a full-blown ecstatic dance party for one.)

(Brian and Bridget try to get her attention, but she doesn't acknowledge them. They give in to the music and start to dance

with her, Brian doing his best chicken neck and Bridget awkwardly bobbing.)

(Becca's dancing grows in intensity and beauty. Bridget and Brian pause and watch her for a second. They share a look and decide to go, leaving Becca to do what she does best. At the end of the dance, Becca sits back down and smiles, a really, truly happy smile for the first time in a long time. Lights fade. End of play.)

The Author Speaks

What inspired you to write this play?
This play was part of a collective exercise in a Theater for Young Audiences class I took my last summer at Hollins University. As a group, we decided to write a series of plays that dealt with a topic teenagers struggled with in today's society. To our surprise, a very common response from the teens we polled was that they struggled with their parents' expectations of who they were and who they should become. I've always been more of an artsy person, and less of a math-brained person, so I wanted to write a play about the value of expression through art and how it can be looked down upon in a society so dominated by numbers and equations. This play is also dear to my heart because Becca was inspired by someone I actually know, and who went through this struggle herself.

Have you dealt with the same theme in other works that you have written?
I write a lot of history-based plays, so this particular piece was a bit of a departure for me. I'm also new to the realm of ten-minute plays, and it was surprising to me how difficult it is to write a cohesive story with a beginning, middle, and end in eight pages. I'm a big fan of the concept of "hope," though. Even if it's not fully realized at the end of my work, I like for the kernel of hope to be out there, and I wanted Becca to find hope and to be able to hold onto it. Life is terribly dark, and I like to leave a little more light whenever I get the chance through my writing.

What writers have had the most profound effect on your style?
I draw a lot from Tennessee Williams. *The Glass Menagerie* is my favorite play. I also draw a lot from Paula Vogel and Arthur Miller. I like to incorporate memory and ghosts into my plays, and not just ghosts of the dead, but also of the living. Sometimes the ghosts of the living can be far more damaging than the ghosts of the dead, as seen through Becca's siblings in *The Dance We Do.*

What do you hope to achieve with this work?
The teenage years are not easy, for a multitude of reasons. I want to let kids who are entering those years and going through them know that it's okay to pursue your passions, and it's okay if you're not an exact copy of your siblings. There is value in so many things, whether it be math and/or art. I want those kids to know that someone sees them and supports them, even if it feels like the rest of the world is against them. That's all I ever wanted to tell the friend Becca is based on, that "I see you." After the staged reading of the play at Mill Mountain Theatre in the summer of 2014, an older man in the audience said the piece really resonated with him because he was the only actor in his family, and the rest of the family didn't understand. He shared this with tears in his eyes, and that moment right there was why I wrote the piece. *The Dance We Do* is specifically geared towards a teenage audience, but I know it resonates with a larger audience of multiple ages.

What were the biggest challenges involved in the writing of this play?
This was the first 10-minute play I'd written to be read and produced. I've written other 10-minute outings for assignments, but they were never meant to be anything more. I am a naturally wordy person. (In school, I was known as the

girl who wrote a 50-page story about the Titanic as opposed to the five pages required by the assignment.) Drafting a concise story in 10 minutes was a challenge, because you have to know the heart of the story and how to get there as quickly as possible. There's also the challenge of how much you reveal when, and what should remain a mystery. It's all the regular challenges of writing a play condensed into a much shorter time frame, which seems to make it a thousand times more difficult, at least for me. Once I'd done it, though, and conquered this mountain, I felt such a sense of accomplishment. A 10-minute play, when done correctly, packs such a powerful punch.

What are the most common mistakes that occur in productions of your work?
Through my work with the Heritage Alliance, I have the great pleasure to be able to produce most of my own work and act in it, so I have yet to gain much experience when it comes to others producing my work. I know that I can be a bit of a control freak—I think it's the stage manager in me. I do struggle with phrasing lines how I want them to be spoken/acted. When I read things with my husband, and I say a line a certain way, he'll tell me to go back and make sure that's how I've written it, because no other actor is going to know to interpret it that way if I don't provide them with clues.

What inspired you to become a playwright?
I love writing, and I love theatre. I've been acting since I was very young. I've also been writing since I was very young. I wrote my first novel at the age of 12. Most of my writing until I entered college was poetry or prose. It wasn't until college that I took a playwriting class and realized that it's a perfect vehicle to combine my three big loves of theatre, writing, and

history. It's the perfect marriage of all the things that make me really excited.

How did you research the subject?

The overall subject matter of parental pressure was picked by the Theatre for Young Audiences class I was in my last summer at Hollins University. As a group, we knew we wanted to approach this topic from multiple viewpoints, and I was struck with a memory I had of a friend who didn't quite fit in with the rest of her family, a girl I wished I'd stuck up for more when she was struggling to find her place in the world. (She's a very accomplished teacher now, and she still dances, so no worries there.) Some things stay with us, like snippets of overheard conversations, or the bad feeling in the pit of your stomach when you don't say something or do something for another person. I also wanted to approach the topic from another angle, and I knew no one else was using parental pressure funneled through siblings.

Are any characters modeled after real life or historical figures?

The characters of Becca, Brian, and Bridget are all based on a family I grew up with. We're old family friends. They're very loving and good people, but "Becca" was very different from her siblings, and her parents were never sure how to handle that. This play is based on small moments I observed growing up alongside them. Amy is not directly based on me, but she does say some of the things I wish I'd said to my "Becca" while she was going through it.

Shakespeare gave advice to the players in *Hamlet*; if you could give advice to your cast what would it be?

Brian and Bridget are not evil. They're memories, or living ghosts. Specifically, they are Becca's memories, and sometimes people have the ability to remember the worst about another person. The Brian and Bridget in this play are the worst versions of themselves, but that's not to say the bullying was all in Becca's mind, because it very much happened. Did Brian and Bridget know how much what they were saying was affecting Becca? They probably weren't aware of the full extent of it, no. When everything is said and done, Brian and Bridget, like most siblings, have Becca's best interests at heart, and this becomes apparent when they leave at the end of the play to let Becca soar. Becca does not soar because they're gone, though, but because she realizes, even when they're still present, that she can be herself and that there's beauty in being different.

About the Author

Anne G'Fellers-Mason holds an undergraduate degree in theatre and history from Mars Hill University and a Masters in history from East Tennessee State University, and is pursuing a Masters in Fine Arts in playwriting from Hollins University. Her one-act, *The War to End All Wars*, received a staged reading at Mars Hill University. Another one-act, *While Sitting in the Park Today*, made it into the semi-finals of the National One-Act Play competition. Anne works for the Heritage Alliance of Northeast Tennessee and Southwest Virginia in Jonesborough, Tennessee, where she creates original, historical pieces about the history all around her. She travels with her one-woman show, *A Sojourn in Jonesborough*, and her cemetery play, *A Spot on the Hill*, entertains audience members in the Old Jonesborough Cemetery during the cooler months. When she's not writing plays, Anne's busy working on one of her many novels in progress.

About YouthPLAYS

YouthPLAYS (www.youthplays.com) is a publisher of award-winning professional dramatists and talented new discoveries, each with an original theatrical voice, and all dedicated to expanding the vocabulary of theatre for young actors and audiences. On our website you'll find one-act and full-length plays and musicals for teen and pre-teen (and even college) actors, as well as duets and monologues for competition. Many of our authors' works have been widely produced at high schools and middle schools, youth theatres and other TYA companies, both amateur and professional, as well as at elementary schools, camps, churches and other institutions serving young audiences and/or actors worldwide. Most are intended for performance by young people, while some are intended for adult actors performing for young audiences.

YouthPLAYS was co-founded by professional playwrights Jonathan Dorf and Ed Shockley. It began merely as an additional outlet to market their own works, which included a substantial body of award-winning published and unpublished plays and musicals. Those interested in their published plays were directed to the respective publishers' websites, and unpublished plays were made available in electronic form. But when they saw the desperate need for material for young actors and audiences—coupled with their experience that numerous quality plays for young people weren't finding a home—they made the decision to represent the work of other playwrights as well. Dozens and dozens of authors are now members of the YouthPLAYS family, with scripts available both electronically and in traditional acting editions. We continue to grow as we look for exciting and challenging plays and musicals for young actors and audiences.

About ProduceaPlay.com

Let's put up a play! Great idea! But producing a play takes time, energy and knowledge. While finding the necessary time and energy is up to you, ProduceaPlay.com is a website designed to assist you with that third element: knowledge.

Created by YouthPLAYS' co-founders, Jonathan Dorf and Ed Shockley, ProduceaPlay.com serves as a resource for producers at all levels as it addresses the many facets of production. As Dorf and Shockley speak from their years of experience (as playwrights, producers, directors and more), they are joined by a group of award-winning theatre professionals and experienced teachers from the world of academic theatre, all making their expertise available for free in the hope of helping this and future generations of producers, whether it's at the school or university level, or in community or professional theatres.

The site is organized into a series of major topics, each of which has its own page that delves into the subject in detail, offering suggestions and links for further information. For example, Publicity covers everything from Publicizing Auditions to How to Use Social Media to Posters to whether it's worth hiring a publicist. Casting details Where to Find the Actors, How to Evaluate a Resume, Callbacks and even Dealing with Problem Actors. You'll find guidance on your Production Timeline, The Theater Space, Picking a Play, Budget, Contracts, Rehearsing the Play, The Program, House Management, Backstage, and many other important subjects.

The site is constantly under construction, so visit often for the latest insights on play producing, and let it help make your play production dreams a reality.

More from YouthPLAYS

Youth on the Roof by Laura King

Play Collection. 55-65 minutes. 3-14 females, 1-9 males (4-16 performers possible).

It's the end of high school, and on the rooftops of schools, apartments, garages and more, the teenagers in these six plays are literally and figuratively standing on the edge of the precipice. Whether it's choosing whether to stay home or venture into the unknown, finding the courage to persevere in the face of failure, or asking themselves if they are truly becoming who they want to be, confronting their futures and that first step into adulthood will require a leap of faith.

The Matsuyama Mirror by Velina Hasu Houston

Drama. 60-70 minutes. 4 females, 1 male, 3 either.

In Matsuyama, Japan in the 1600s, a world before the discovery of mirrors, young Aiko comes of age in the aftermath of her mother's death. Gifted with a "magic" mirror, she sees her image and believes that it is her mother's spirit—and when her father remarries and she begins to grow up, Aiko resists, escaping into an enchanted world where dolls come to life. As they encourage her to stay to play and frolic, will Aiko fall into the fantasy forever, or will she discover the true magic of life?

The Exceptional Childhood Center by Dylan Schifrin

Comedy. 25-35 minutes. 2-4 females, 2-3 males (5-6 performers possible).

Reggie Watson has been accepted into the right preschool. He's set for life…as long as he can make it through the one-day trial period. But when desperation breeds disaster and his future hangs in the balance, Reggie and his band of quirky classmates may just discover things about themselves that school could never teach them.

Mi Coche, Mi Quince by Susan Lieberman
Dramedy. 95-110 minutes. 5-12+ females, 3-8+ males (8-20+ performers possible).

Luis, a high school senior and the pillar of his fractured Mexican-American family, is set to play a key role in his sister Ana's upcoming quinceañera celebration. But when his girlfriend Miriam discovers that she is pregnant, Luis' future plans and Ana's *quince* dreams are derailed. As Miriam explores adoption, further challenging the cultural conventions of their community and testing Luis' commitment to the relationship, Ana's traditional rite of passage may just become a time of unexpected transformation for everyone.

La Bella Cinderella by Claudia Haas
Comedy. 50-60 minutes. 3-4 females, 2-3 males (6 performers total, plus optional extras).

The Primo Pasta Players turn the Cinderella tale topsy-turvy with their own brand of zany, pasta-loving fun. Help the Players get ready for the ball, save our heroine from a wild boar, and stop the villainous clown from stealing the crown. There are opportunities to add music and dance, and in the end, silly rules the land!

HKFN: The Abbreviated Adventures of Huckleberry Finn by Jeff Goode
Comedy. 25-35 minutes. 3-8 females, 2-6 males (5-10 performers possible).

The actor playing Huck runs away from a production of Twain's controversial classic, *The Adventures of Huckleberry Finn*. But when the actor who plays Jim runs away too and troublemakers Duke & King join in, their fugitive theatre company launches into a series of misadventures—while the domineering Aunt Polly tries to force them back into the "real" play. In the chaos, that play—and its discussion about race—may be happening without them knowing it.

Made in the USA
Columbia, SC
12 August 2017